OPPENHEIMER.

Charles Scribner's Sons, New York

OPPENHEIMER

I. I. Rabi

Robert Serber

Victor F. Weisskopf

Abraham Pais

Glenn T. Seaborg

PUBLISHER'S PREFACE

THIS BOOK was "built," as publishers say. The text originated as a series of lectures given by J. Robert Oppenheimer's friends and colleagues at the Oppenheimer Memorial Session of the American Physical Society meeting, Washington, D. C., April 24, 1967. Because of the high degree of excellence of the material and the interest in and importance of the subject, the authors and the publisher decided that the speeches should be preserved in book form, and they have been edited accordingly.

I. I. Rabi, who was to have spoken at the APS meeting but was prevented by other commitments from doing so, has contributed an Introduction to the volume, covering those aspects of Oppenheimer's life that he would have discussed at the meeting. The Oppenheimer Chronology and the Selected Bibliography of Oppenheimer's Writings were assembled by the editors of *Physics Today* for the October 1967 issue of that journal, in which the four speeches were first published. The Glossary was prepared especially for the book by Dr. Grace Marmor Spruch of the New York University Department of Physics, to make the essays more accessible to the general reader. The Biographical Notes were also especially prepared for the book, and an index has been included.

When speeches are published first as magazine articles and later in book form, the authors and publishers have an opportunity at each stage to add new material—explanations in the text, footnotes, reference notes—and in general to clarify and round out the original spoken words. This is what has happened here. In addition, the book offers for the first time a section of important and little-known photographs from the private collection of Mrs. J. Robert Oppenheimer, who generously made them available, and others from the private collections of the authors, including a few by the celebrated photographer Alfred Eisenstaedt.

This book makes what educators describe as a contribution. Although short, it is the first significant biography of Oppenheimer since his death, and it treats Oppenheimer in a different way than has been done heretofore, since his life and especially his work are described by fellow scientists who knew him well and worked with him closely. Obviously, there will be other biographies of Oppenheimer, but for the time being this one fills a need and constitutes one of the best available accounts.

CONTENTS

CONTENTS

ILLUSTRATIONS

I. I. RABI

Introduction

ROBERT OPPENHEIMER was one of the most highly regarded personalities in the civilized world. His presence in almost any country attracted public attention both from the press and from individuals. I have been in restaurants with him, even in small airports, and always people came up and respectfully asked for his autograph. In many ways he held a position in public esteem of the nature of that held by Gandhi or Einstein. Plays based on the public record of his secret trial attract audiences both in Europe and in the United States. The result of the trial, which was deprivation of his clearance to access to classified information, was, and still is, generally regarded as an example of the moral insensitivity of some important elements in United States government circles rather than as a reflection on Oppenheimer's character or loyalty.

For the first half of this century the scientific community of the United States, and more especially the physicists, did not lack for strong and respected leadership. One recalls the giant figures of Henry Rowland, Michael Pupin, A. A. Michelson, Robert Millikan, Karl Compton, who both led and dominated the physics community. This leadership was generally accepted by the physicists, by the press and by the public at large. By 1946, with the end of the war and the retirement from activity of the older leadership, this mantle naturally fell on the shoulders of Robert Oppenheimer. Although other eminent scientists exerted strong influences—for example, Ernest O. Lawrence, Harold Urey, Arthur Compton,

Lee A. DuBridge, and James B. Conant—Oppenheimer's leadership was recognized more universally, both at home and abroad, even though he held no high position such as Conant's and was not the recipient of extraordinary scientific honors.

This rise to public eminence and recognition was quite sudden and was not presaged by events preceding the war. At that time Oppenheimer's reputation and influence were centered around the small and close circle of physicists. As the wartime director of the Los Alamos Laboratory, which made the atomic bomb, he was bound to receive important public attention, but there were other directors of great laboratories, and other physicists, who shared equal esteem but did not become objects of such general interest. Oppenheimer, after Einstein, emerged as the great charismatic figure of the scientific world.

Oppenheimer's scientific biography and his public services are outlined in the essays that follow. In this Introduction, I will trace Oppenheimer's earlier life and the development of personality and achievement that made it almost inevitable for him to become the important and interesting figure he was. I know very little of his student years except that he was very precocious. My wife, who was in some classes with him at the well-known Ethical Culture School in New York City, remembers him as brilliant and as being so recognized by the whole school. From conversations with him I have the impression that his own regard for the school was not affectionate. Too great a dose of ethical culture can often sour the budding intellectual who would prefer a more profound approach to human relations and man's place in the universe.

My first acquaintance with him came late in 1928 in Werner Heisenberg's Institute at the University of Leipzig,

4

where we were both visiting. His reputation had preceded him. Even as a graduate student at the University of Göttingen, he was well known for brilliance in physics, and his sharp wit as well. His lanky, slouching figure, his reserved air, the penetrating gaze of his blue eyes, and the striking phrases that came out in a soft, yet audible voice, made him a center of attention in almost any company. Wolfgang Pauli, Jr., who had already achieved eminence at that time, made him a prize subject of his imitations of various personalities in physics, of which he was very proud.

My longest period of close personal interaction with Oppenheimer came in the spring of 1929 when he and I were both in Zurich at Pauli's Institute at the E.T.H. (*Eidgenossische Technische Hochschule*). Oppenheimer worked very hard that spring but had a gift of concealing his assiduous application with an air of easy nonchalance. Actually, he was engaged in a very difficult calculation of the opacity of surfaces of stars to their internal radiation, an important constant in the theoretical construction of stellar models. He spoke little of these problems and seemed to be much more interested in literature, especially the Hindu classics and the more esoteric Western writers. At Harvard he was a contributor to *Hound and Horn*, an intellectual magazine now long extinct. Of politics and music, which occupied him so greatly in the late 1930s, and for the rest of his life, he showed little or no interest or knowledge. Pauli once remarked to me that Oppenheimer seemed to treat physics as an avocation and psychoanalysis as a vocation. As I shared many of his interests, I found him a delightful and fascinating companion. Even at that time his presence conveyed a sense of excitement and heightened awareness that was such a great asset to the School of Theoretical Physics he later founded at the University of California.

During the same period I had the pleasure of meeting his parents, Mr. and Mrs. Julius Oppenheimer, who were delightful persons of great cultivation and taste. They gathered a small collection of excellent paintings, which included several Cézannes; Robert Oppenheimer was very fond of these paintings, some of which he inherited. Although he was greatly interested in painting, to the best of my knowledge he never used his own means to add to this collection, an interesting circumstance I never discussed with him.

At the end of that spring semester I returned to Columbia and Oppenheimer to California. Since Oppenheimer rarely came to meetings and travel money was not easy to obtain then, we rarely saw one another but maintained a feeling of intimacy that enabled us to resume where we left off on the occasions when we did meet. His students I saw more frequently and could not fail to be impressed with the power of his personality, which affected them to such a degree that one could often hear his cadences and quality of voice when a member of his school was heard from a distance or through the open door of another room. Pauli once remarked that the Oppenheimer students, when regarding a problem, first thought of how Oppenheimer would go about it before they began to rely on their own powers. This was much more true of the students of his earlier years than of those who came later.

Oppenheimer understood the whole structure of physics with extraordinary clarity, and not only the structure, but the interactions between the different elements. Hardly any branch of physics was foreign to him. As well as theoretical physics, he also had a vast knowledge of experimental results and methods at his fingertips and would continually amaze experimenters by his great knowledge of their own subject— in some respects exceeding their own, especially in fields of great current interest. It is therefore not surprising that he became an almost mythical figure, especially to experimenters. He could display his great knowledge in their own fields but then could take off into the blue of abstract theory where they could not follow, or only with great difficulty.

One often wonders why men of Oppenheimer's gifts do not discover everything worth discovering, why important problems are still left to solve. With the vast intellectual arsenal at his disposal there were important questions in physics in which Oppenheimer worked diligently, where he was very often on the track of the solutions, and where his taste in the selection of the questions was impeccable, and yet as in the case of quantum electrodynamics the definite solutions came from others. In pondering this subject it seems to me that in some respects Oppenheimer was over-educated in those fields which lie outside the scientific tradition, such as his interest in religion, in the Hindu religion in particular, which resulted in a feeling for the mystery of the universe that surrounded him almost like a fog. He saw physics clearly, looking toward what had already been done, but at the border he tended to feel that there was much more of the mysterious and novel than there actually was. He was insufficiently confident of the power of the intellectual tools he already possessed and did not drive his thought to the very end because he felt instinctively that new ideas and new methods were necessary to go further than he and his students had already gone. Some may call it a lack of faith, but in my opinion it was more a turning away from the hard, crude methods of theoretical physics into a mystical realm of broad intuition. Pauli had perhaps a more specific mystical bent of mind and was greatly intrigued by some of the archetypal ideas of Kepler, but his hard logic drove him forward, nevertheless, until his invention in a particular field was exhausted.

In writing about Oppenheimer I have been reminded of the remarks made by a classmate in my freshman year at Cornell. Physically and perhaps intellectually and emotionally, he was very like Oppenheimer. One day he announced: "I give the lie to the materialist. I am a disembodied spirit." In Oppenheimer the element of earthiness was feeble.

Yet it was essentially this spiritual quality, this refinement as expressed in speech and manner, that was the basis of his charisma. He never expressed himself completely. He always left a feeling that there were depths of sensibility and insight not yet revealed. These may be the qualities of the born leader who seems to have reserves of uncommitted strength. That Oppenheimer had these reserves was clearly demonstrated when he was given the directorship of the Los Alamos Laboratory by that eccentric administrative genius, General Leslie R. Groves. A less likely choice on the basis of personality and experience could hardly be imagined. Yet calling on these very reserves he constructed the laboratory from the ground up and made it into a most effective and deadly instrument for the application of science to destruction. At the same time, with no deviation from its dread purpose of making the atomic bomb, he created an atmosphere of excitement, enthusiasm, and high intellectual and moral purpose that still remains with those who participated as one of the great experiences of their lives.

ROBERT SERBER

The Early Years

THE YEARS 1925 TO 1929 were great years in physics. They saw the development of the quantum theory: the Schrödinger equation, the Dirac equation, field theory and quantum electrodynamics. That it was so completely a European development illustrates the weakness and provincialism of theoretical physics in the United States at the time. Within fifteen years the situation was drastically changed, and American theoretical physics was becoming comparable to the best. A very important element in this change was the influence of Robert Oppenheimer. The alumni of the great school of theoretical physics he established in Berkeley, California, played a large part in the subsequent development of American physics and also in enabling us to meet the demands of World War II.

Oppenheimer was a little too young to participate in the original flowering of quantum mechanics. He received his B.A. from Harvard in 1925, spent the next two years in Cambridge, England, and Göttingen, and was awarded his Ph.D. in Göttingen in 1927. In 1928 he was at Harvard and Caltech as a National Research Fellow, and in 1929 at Leyden and Zurich as a Fellow of the International Education Board. Oppenheimer's first paper, in 1926, dealt with molecular energy levels,[1] his second with transitions to continuum states in hydrogenic atoms.[2] Then at Göttingen he wrote his famous paper with Max Born on the approximations involved in the theory of molecules.[3] During the next three years he wrote a series of papers mostly depending on his knowledge of the

11

continuum wave functions, which he appears to have been the first to master. He discussed their normalization, and calculated the absorption coefficient of X rays near the K-edge; the continuous X-ray spectrum; and the elastic and inelastic scattering of electrons, including the first treatment of the exchange effects. He also greatly improved the calculation of stellar opacities. His most original contribution, however, was his theory of field emission, the first example of an effect due to barrier penetration (antedating the explanation of radioactive alpha decay). He developed a perturbation theory of nonorthogonal states, and used it to calculate the disintegration of a hydrogen atom in an electric field. He then applied his results to the field emission effects observed in metals. This was done at Pasadena, where Millikan and Charles C. Lauritsen were studying the phenomenon and was the first evidence of a feature later to be so prominent in his work, his close collaboration with his experimental colleagues.

Oppenheimer's early work showed power and facility, but after his year with Pauli in 1928–29 his interests changed and thereafter were devoted to the more fundamental questions of physics. At Zurich he learned of Heisenberg and Pauli's work on quantum electrodynamics, and in late 1929 he published his paper on resonance scattering of light in which he attempted to deal with the self-energy difficulties.[4] The hope was that the frequencies would remain finite, even though the energies had infinite shifts, but this did not turn out to be the case. The way in which the shifts differ for states of different energy was not understood until nearly twenty years later. Oppenheimer did observe that the leading divergent terms were equal for states of the same energy and pointed out that the applicability of the theory to the fine-structure splitting could be ascribed to this circumstance.

PROTON AND ANTIPROTON

Early in 1930, Oppenheimer showed that the positive particles of the Dirac theory must have the same mass as the electron and thus could not be protons as Dirac had suggested.[5] His argument was that matrix elements of the current between positive and negative energy states contributed importantly to the scattering of light by both particles and antiparticles. Since the matrix elements were the same, it was impossible to understand how the Thomson formula with the electron mass would hold for the positive energy states and the Thomson formula with the proton mass for the negative energy states.

He also calculated the lifetime for annihilation of particles and antiparticles; since the matrix elements involved were similar to those in Thomson scattering, there could be no reason to doubt the short lifetime for annihilation that resulted. He concluded that the proton must be an independent elementary particle and have its own antiparticle. This was the first prediction of the antiproton.

Oppenheimer then turned to the problem of the anomalous absorption of ThC'' gamma rays which had first been reported by S. H. Chao, working at Caltech; and with Harvey Hall he calculated the relativistic photoeffect.[6] An error led them to the conclusion that the Dirac theory must be wrong for energies greater than mc^2, and was probably responsible for Oppenheimer's failure at that time to be convinced of the reality of the positron. In 1931, he attempted to linearize the theory of the photon—as Dirac had done for the electron —and pointed out the different structure of the theory for particles of integral and half-integral spins, the difference that later was the basis of Pauli's proof of the connection between spin and statistics.

In 1932, J. Franklin Carlson and Oppenheimer, in an effort to understand the great penetration of cosmic rays, studied the ionization losses of relativistic electrons and Pauli neutrinos. (The latter particles, suggested by Pauli, were supposed to approximate the electrons in mass, have a small magnetic moment, and be a constituent of nuclei.) They concluded that neither electrons nor magnetic neutrinos should have the properties of the penetrating component.

In 1933, after the discovery of the positron by Carl D. Anderson, Oppenheimer and Milton S. Plesset gave the first correct description of the mechanism of pair production by gamma rays and showed that the theory quantitatively explained the excess absorption of ThC'' gamma rays in heavy elements.[7] However, they pointed out that the theory would predict large deviations from the mass-absorption law for cosmic rays—assuming, as they did, that the sea-level cosmic rays were mostly electrons and positrons, and concluded that, while the theory was applicable in the range of radioactive-decay energies, it must fail at energies greater than $137 \ mc^2$. A fundamental barrier to Oppenheimer's success in making progress with the difficulties of quantum electrodynamics must have been this belief in the incorrectness of the theory, a belief he continually stressed. His appreciation of experimental results and his close association with experimental physicists, a strength in other aspects of his work, in this may have been a weakness.

FIELD THEORY

Later in 1933, in a paper with Wendell H. Furry, Oppenheimer formulated the Dirac theory as a field theory, essentially in its modern form.[8] The charge-renormalization and the vacuum-polarization effects were pointed out, although gauge invariance remained a problem. The vacuum-polarization effects were declared to be observable, with a warning that other radiative corrections existed for electrons. Similar considerations were being made by Dirac at about the same time. During 1934 and 1935, Oppenheimer worked on critiques of this and other aspects of electrodynamics. In June 1936, he first discussed the theory of electron-positron showers, and an elegant treatment of this important problem was given at the end of the year by Carlson and Oppenheimer[9] and then by Hartland Snyder, one of his students. Oppenheimer concluded that the success of the shower theory proved the validity of electron theory and required the existence of a new type of particle in cosmic rays. In June 1937, immediately after the discovery of the meson by Anderson, Seth H. Neddermeyer, Jabez C. Street, and Stevenson, he wrote a paper with me pointing[10] out the probable connection of the cosmic-ray meson with the particle suggested by Hideki Yukawa, drawing the inference that it was not a primary cosmic ray but was ejected from nuclei in the upper atmosphere, and explaining the showers below sea level as being produced by knock-on electrons, recoiling from collisions with mesons. Another suggestion originally in this paper—that the finite lifetime of the meson would lead to anomalous atmospheric absorption—was eliminated on Millikan's insistence of the validity of the mass-absorption law.

In 1939, in a paper with Snyder and me, Oppenheimer returned to the question of the soft component below sea level and pointed out that if the mesons had spin one they would radiate too rapidly.[11] This conclusion was conditional on the convergence of electrodynamic theory for spin-one particles. Two of Oppenheimer's students, Robert F. Christy and Siuchi Kusaka, then studied the question in more detail and arrived at the same conclusion. In 1941, after Marcel Schein, William P. Jesse and Ernest O. Wollan had shown that the primary cosmic rays were predominantly protons, Oppenheimer and Christy suggested that the soft component at high altitude could be accounted for if, in addition to the penetrating mesons, there were roughly equal numbers of fast-decaying mesons, with a lifetime of about 10^{-8} seconds, that decayed into electrons or positrons.[12] Oppenheimer's later clarification, in 1947, of the role of the π^0 in the generation of the soft component was a natural sequel to this earlier work.

NUCLEAR REACTIONS

Earlier, Oppenheimer had become involved in the work in nuclear physics being done by the rapidly growing schools of Lawrence in Berkeley and Lauritsen in Pasadena. His first paper on this subject, in December 1932, accounted for the results of Malcolm Henderson on the energy variation of the nuclear reaction produced by bombarding lithium by protons.[13] In 1935, with Melba Phillips, he calculated the yield of protons in deuteron reactions, the "Oppenheimer-Phillips process," [14] which explained the experimental results of Lawrence, Edwin M. McMillan and Robert L. Thornton. A series of papers on reactions in light elements discussed observations of the Lauritsen group.[15] In one of them the first evidence for the operation of an isotopic spin selection rule was pointed out.

Oppenheimer's connections at Pasadena with the staff of the Mt. Wilson Observatory and with Richard Tolman led to an interest in astrophysics and general relativity, to papers on neutron stars in 1938 and 1939,[16] and to his well-known work with Snyder on gravitational contraction in 1939.[17]

The years 1940 and 1941 saw intensive work on meson theory, including attempts to deal with the strong coupling problem by including inertial and radiative-reaction damping effects. In 1941, in a paper with Julian Schwinger,[18] he applied Gregor Wentzel's strong coupling theory to pseudoscalar mesons, and predicted the existence of nucleon isobars with an excitation energy slightly less than the rest energy of the meson. Multiple-meson production was also discussed. These efforts continued until interrupted by World War II.

OPPIE AS A TEACHER

Oppenheimer's fascinating personality played a major part in his unique powers as a teacher. I can cite my own experience, the impact of my first meeting with him. In 1934, I received my Ph.D. working under Professor John H. Van Vleck at the University of Wisconsin, and a National Research Fellowship that I intended to spend at an Eastern university. On the way East from Wisconsin I stopped at Ann Arbor to spend a month at the summer session. Oppenheimer was there, and after hearing him lecture and spending a little time with him, I reversed my direction and went to Berkeley. When I arrived I discovered that most of the National Research Fellows in theoretical physics were already there.

By this time Oppenheimer's course in quantum mechanics was well established. Oppie* (as he was known to his Berkeley students) was quick, impatient, and had a sharp tongue. In the earliest days of his teaching he was reputed to have ter-

---

* This spelling of Oppenheimer's nickname was a corruption of the original nickname, acquired in Leyden. Oppenheimer himself used the form "Opje," as did all his early students.

rorized the students. Now, after five years of experience, he had mellowed—if his earlier students were to be believed. His course was an inspirational, as well as educational achievement. He transmitted to his students a feeling of the beauty of the logical structure of physics and an excitement in the development of the science. Almost everyone listened to the course more than once, and Oppie occasionally had difficulty in dissuading students from coming a third or fourth time. The basic logic of Oppenheimer's course in quantum mechanics derived from Pauli's article in the *Handbuch der Physik*.[19] Its graduates, Leonard Schiff in particular, carried it, each in his own version, to many campuses.

Oppie's way of working with his research students was also original. His group would consist of eight or ten graduate students and about a half dozen postdoctoral fellows. He would meet the group once a day in his office. A little before the appointed time its members would straggle in and dispose themselves on the tables and about the walls. Oppie would come in and discuss with one after another the status of the student's research problem, while the others listened and offered comments. All were exposed to a broad range of topics. Oppenheimer was interested in everything, and one subject after another was introduced and coexisted with all the others. In an afternoon we might discuss electrodynamics, cosmic rays, astrophysics and nuclear physics.

Oppie's relations with his students were not confined to office and classroom. He was a bachelor then, and a part of his social life was intertwined with ours. Often we worked late and continued the discussion through dinner and then later at his apartment on Shasta Road. When we tired of our problems, or cleaned up the point at issue, the talk would turn to art, music, literature, and politics. If the work was going badly we might give up and go to a movie. Sometimes we took a night off and had a Mexican dinner in Oakland or went to a good restaurant in San Francisco. In the early days this meant taking the Berkeley ferry and a ride across the bay. The ferries back to Berkeley didn't run very often late at night, and this required passing the time waiting for them at the bars and night clubs near the ferry dock. Frequently we missed several ferries. Ed McMillan was often our companion on these adventures.

We held regular joint seminars with Felix Bloch and his students from Stanford. Afterward, Oppie would frequently treat the whole entourage to dinner at Jack's in San Francisco. These were postdepression days, and students were poor. The world of good food and good wines and gracious living was far from the experience of many of them, and Oppie was introducing them to an unfamiliar way of life. We acquired something of his tastes. We went to concerts together and listened to chamber music. Oppie and Arn Nordsieck read Plato in the original Greek. There were many evening parties where we drank and talked and danced until late, and where, when Oppie was supplying the food, the novices suffered from the hot chili that social example required them to eat.

During this time Oppie was a professor at both Berkeley and Caltech (where his name metamorphized into Robert). The arrangement was made possible because the Berkeley spring semester ended early in April, and Robert could then teach the spring quarter in Pasadena. Many of his students made the annual trek with him. Some things were easier in those days. We thought nothing of giving up our houses or apartments in Berkeley, confident that we could find a garden cottage in Pasadena for twenty-five dollars a month. We didn't own more than could be packed in the back of a car. In Pasadena, in addition to being exposed to new information on physics, we led an active social life. The Tolmans were good friends, and we had very warm relations with Charlie Lauritsen and his group. Willy Fowler was a graduate student then, and Tommy Lauritsen was still in high school. We spent many evenings at the Mexican restaurants on Olvera Street and many nights partying in Charlie Lauritsen's garden. In 1940 Robert married, and our relationship was further enriched by the friendship of his lovely and gracious wife, Kitty.

One feature of the times which contrasts with present customs was the relatively little personal contact we had with the outer world of physics. The meetings we went to were the West Coast meetings of the American Physical Society. The first conference I can recall was a Cosmic Ray Symposium in Chicago to which Oppie and I drove from his New Mexico ranch in the early summer of 1939. We had a few visitors, however. Niels Bohr, Dirac, and Pauli made short visits to Berkeley or Pasadena, and I met Victor Weisskopf, Hans Bethe, George Placzek, George Gamow and Walter Elsasser at the ranch.

Many facets of Oppenheimer's character contributed to his greatness as a teacher: his great capacity as a physicist, his wide intellectual interests, his astonishing quickness of mind, his great gift for expression, his sensitive perception, his social presence, which made him the center of every gathering. His students emulated him as best they could. They copied his gestures, his mannerisms, his intonations. He truly influenced their lives. Among his prewar students (besides some I have already mentioned) were Leo Nedelsky, Glenn Camp, Ed Uehling, Fritz Kalckar, George Volkoff, Sid Dancoff, Phil Morrison, Joe Keller, Willis Lamb, Bernard Peters, Bill Rarita, Eldred Nelson, Stan Frankel, Joe Weinberg, and Chaim Richman. All of us owe him more than we can say for his instruction, for his friendship and affection. For us his death was a great blow and a great loss.

Oppenheimer in Geneva at the international laboratory CERN (Conseil Européen pour la Recherche Nucléaire—European Organization for Nuclear Research), 1962 (Courtesy CERN/PIO)

At the San Diego, California, zoo during a meeting of the American
Physical Society, 1938. *Left to right*: Robert Serber, W. A. Fowler,
Oppenheimer, L. W. Alvarez (Courtesy Mrs. J. Robert Oppenheimer)

The scientific staff of the University of California Radiation Laboratory with the magnet of the unfinished 60-inch cyclotron, 1938. *Left to right and top to bottom:* A. S. Langsdorf, S. J. Simmons, J. G. Hamilton, D. H. Sloan, Oppenheimer, W. M. Brobeck, R. Cornog, R. R. Wilson, E. Viez, J. J. Livingood, J. Backus, W. B. Mann, P. C. Aebersold, E. M. McMillan, E. M. Lyman, M. D. Kamen, D. C. Kalbfell, W. W. Salisbury, J. H. Lawrence, R. Serber, F. N. D. Kurie, R. T. Birge, E. O. Lawrence, D. C. Cooksey, A. H. Snell, L. W. Alvarez, P. H. Abelson (Courtesy Lawrence Radiation Laboratory)

Oppenheimer and his horse, Crisis, at his New Mexico ranch, c. 1940 (Courtesy Mrs. J. Robert Oppenheimer)

With Julian Schwinger, at the Oppenheimer home on Eagle Hill, Berkeley, California, c. 1941 (Courtesy Mrs. J. Robert Oppenheimer)

With the 184-inch cyclotron magnet, 1946. *Left to right:* E. O. Lawrence, G. T. Seaborg, Oppenheimer (Courtesy Lawrence Radiation Laboratory)

Oppenheimer's hat resting on cyclotron plumbing at the University of California, Berkeley, c. 1946 (Courtesy Mrs. J. Robert Oppenheimer)

At home in Princeton, New Jersey, c. 1948, with his children, Peter and Toni, and (*bottom right*) his dog, Buddy (Courtesy Mrs. J. Robert Oppenheimer)

At the Oppenheimer home in Los Alamos, New Mexico, c. 1944. *Left to right:* I. I. Rabi; D. McKibben, who ran the Laboratory's Santa Fe office; Oppenheimer; Victor F. Weisskopf (Courtesy Los Alamos Scientific Laboratory)

In the common room of the Institute for Advanced Study, Princeton, New Jersey, 1947. *Left to right:* Oppenheimer, P. A. M. Dirac, Abraham Pais (Courtesy Alfred Eisenstaedt/Pix Incorporated)

With Abraham Pais in the seminar room at Fuld Hall, Institute for Advanced Study, 1947 (Courtesy Alfred Eisenstaedt/Pix Incorporated)

The Oppenheimers at a social affair in Rochester, New York, c. 1948 (Courtesy Mrs. J. Robert Oppenheimer)

With Pandit Nehru and Mrs. Oppenheimer at the Oppenheimers'
Princeton home, c. 1952 (Courtesy Mrs. J. Robert Oppenheimer)

In his office at the Institute for Advanced Study, with E. A. Lowe
(Courtesy Mrs. J. Robert Oppenheimer)

With C. F. Powell at the CERN International Conference on High Energy Physics in 1962 (Courtesy CERN/PIO)

Oppenheimer in his office at the Institute for Advanced Study the day after he received the Fermi Award, 1963 (Courtesy Mrs. Ulli Steltzer)

VICTOR F. WEISSKOPF

The Los Alamos Years

IN 1939 Robert Oppenheimer was still intent on the teaching and theoretical work that absorbed his attention during the years before World War II. But 1939 changed many things: It witnessed the beginning of the most destructive war in history. It also changed science. Many physicists who never were interested in applications of science devoted their skills to the necessities of war and became applied physicists. They faced new problems, new experiences, different from the accustomed academic environment.

The deepest change in the character of our science, however, came from the discovery of fission. Many hoped—and Oppenheimer was one of them—that the number of neutrons released would have been small enough to prevent a chain reaction. Yet soon enough it was clear that, on the forefront of the most esoteric and basic part of our science, a phenomenon full of tremendous destructive and constructive potentialities had been discovered. It was not yet ready for exploitation; many staggering problems had to be solved, but the way was clearly indicated. ⌜Many physicists were drawn into this work by fate and destiny rather than enthusiasm. A threat hung over us—the frightening possibility of finding this new and incredibly powerful weapon in the hands of the powers of evil—but there is no doubt that we were also attracted by the unique challenge of dealing with nuclear phenomena on a large scale, with taming an essentially cosmic process.⌝

Oppenheimer was chosen to be leader of the most critical part of the venture: the design of the bomb itself at Los

Alamos. It was an inspired but by no means obvious choice. Certainly he was the central figure in nuclear physics. No other man commanded so much respect of his colleagues; but he never was director of a large research operation, he did not have what one calls "administrative experience." Few people were aware at the outset that Oppenheimer was to create at Los Alamos a new form of scientific life.

I cannot proceed with this description of the Los Alamos period without pointing to a tragic and fateful aspect of human history. Every so often, great ideas, new ventures, and new forms of thinking and acting have been conceived and carried out only when they have had to serve men in their resolve to destroy each other in the name of some cause. At Los Alamos this tragic involvement was painfully obvious.

LOS ALAMOS AND FISSION

The task facing Oppenheimer and his collaborators was stupendous. When the work started at Los Alamos not much more was known than the fundamental ideas of a chain reaction. What happens in a nuclear explosion had to be predicted theoretically in all its aspects for the design of the bomb, since there was no time to wait for experiments; no fissionable material was available yet. The details of the fission process had to be understood. The slowing down of neutrons in matter and the theory of explosions and implosions under completely novel conditions had to be investigated. Nuclear physicists had to become experts in fields of physics and technology unknown to them such as shock waves and hydrodynamics. Oppenheimer directed these studies in the real sense of the words. Here his uncanny speed in grasping the main points of any subject was a decisive factor; he could acquaint himself with the essential details of every part of the work.

He did not direct from the head office. He was intellectually and even physically present at each significant step; he was present in the laboratory or in the seminar rooms when a new effect was measured, when a new idea was conceived. It was not that he contributed so many ideas or suggestions; he did so sometimes, but his main influence came from his continuous and intense presence, which produced a sense of direct participation in all of us. It created that unique atmosphere of enthusiasm and challenge that pervaded the place throughout its time. I remember vividly the sessions of the co-ordinating council, a regular meeting of all group leaders where progress and failures were reviewed and future plans were discussed. The discussions covered everything: physics, technology, organization, administration, secrecy regulations and our relations to the Army.

It was most impressive to see Oppie handle that mixture of international scientific prima donnas, engineers, and army officers, forging them into an enthusiastically productive crowd. The project was not without tensions and clashes between personalities, but he dealt with these problems with a light hand, and he knew how to exploit conflicts in a productive way. I remember the weekly colloquium, where everyone with a white badge—the mark of an academic degree—participated and listened to talks about all essential aspects of the work. Oppenheimer insisted on having these regular colloquia against the opposition of the security-minded people, who wanted each man only to know his part of the work. He knew that each one must know the whole thing if he was to be creative.

IN THE DESERT

Los Alamos was not the first of large collaborative scientific enterprises. World War II produced a number of them in the field of nuclear energy, such as Chicago, Hanford, and Oak Ridge, and in other disciplines as well—the MIT Radiation Laboratory is one important example. Still, I believe that Los Alamos was special and more significant than the others. Many factors contributed to this, all connected with Oppenheimer's personality. The location, which was his own choice, gave it a special character by its romantic isolation in the midst of Indian culture. Living in this unusual landscape, separated from the rest of the world, within walking distance of the laboratories—all this created a community type of living where work and leisure were not separated. But the special flavor came from the kind of people that were there. It was a large community of active scientists, many of them in their most vigorous and productive years. (One can interpret this in many ways; I remember when General Leslie Groves asked Oppie to influence his colleagues in certain ways—he did not want to enlarge the maternity ward of the hospital— Oppenheimer replied, "This seems hardly to be the responsibility of a scientific director.")

The scientists were not all native Americans, some had come to the United States shortly before the war as refugees from Europe; some came from England and other Allied countries to pool their resources. The most famous among them were Enrico Fermi, Rudolf Peierls, William Penney, and, of course, Niels Bohr and his son Aage. The great world of international physics was assembled inside the fence, we felt that that fence kept the rest of the world from us, not us from them. Oppenheimer formed the style of this enterprise in many ways beyond his participation in the work itself. He understood that there was a deep common bond among these scientists that was stronger than any national bond, and he had a lucky hand in making use of this bond for the shaping of an unusually creative social unit. Nobody who was there will ever forget the numerous discussions, public and private, on all subjects of interest: physics, philosophy, social problems, and foremost the great tragedy of war and what it does to mankind. One of the most important factors that kept us at work was the common awareness of the great danger of the bomb in the hands of an irresponsible dictator. After Hitler's defeat, it turned out that this danger was in fact not so great; still, the work and the spirit continued until the task was accomplished—until, in the desert of Alamogordo, for the first time a nuclear fire was kindled by man. All of us, and Oppenheimer more than anyone, were deeply shaken by this event.

Obviously, scientists such as those at Los Alamos would be deeply concerned with the ominous implications of their work. Long before the great test, the political and moral implications of the bomb were in the foreground of interest. Oppenheimer and Bohr started many discussions about the dangers of atomic weapons and about ways and means of turning this new discovery into a constructive force for peace. All of us hoped that this great force of destruction might open the eyes of the world to the futility of war. It was in part Oppie's leadership that led to the formation of groups devoted to these problems and to a number of ideas and plans for an international approach to the exploitation of atomic energy, so that this new force would bring nations together instead of tearing them apart.

We know today how successful Los Alamos was in its primary purpose: the design of a nuclear bomb. We also know that the numerous efforts to end the danger of a future nuclear war were less successful. The predicament in which our country finds itself today is an ominous sign of how little we have learned of the futility of wars.

Physics, science, and human society were different after the nuclear explosion in Alamogordo. Let me comment about the change in physics. I believe that the new ways of big science in nuclear physics and particle physics have been inspired by the Los Alamos venture. I believe that Oppenheimer gave us an example of how large scientific enterprises can be more than the sum of the collaborative effort of their groups. They can be imbued with a creative spirit based upon a common heritage and a common aim. Perhaps the new giant laboratories are beginning to show that great achievements can be accomplished by inspired collaboration of large groups of scientists, without being aimed at war or destruction. Maybe it is the great idea of science as a concern of all men together, a supranational activity, the idea of science as the spearhead of human co-operation across national and political frontiers, that helps to create that spirit of accomplishment.

What this may mean for the future we do not know. We do not know whether the work at Los Alamos has changed the world for better or worse. We cannot make such an assessment now or in the near future; human history is too involved and too contradictory. Inventions conceived for doing good turn out to be destructive and devices made to destroy can sometimes change the world for the better. One thing is certain, however: The achievement of Los Alamos made the world of human relations much more complex than it had been, and we carry a much heavier load of responsibilities on our shoulders. I doubt that we are ready for it. The ordeal that Oppenheimer went through in 1954 is a sad indication of how little some of the people in authority understood the problems involved. Since we live in a democratic society, every one of us must bear part of the blame for the humiliation that this great man had to suffer publicly. Much has to be done to educate ourselves, our fellow citizens, and all humanity, so that we are ready to face our future responsibilities. We are more than ever in need of men with the wisdom and the insight of Robert Oppenheimer.

ABRAHAM PAIS

The Princeton Period

IN SEPTEMBER 1946 the American Physical Society met in midtown Manhattan. The minutes of this meeting note that it "was confined to papers on three topics: cosmic ray phenomena, theories of elementary particles and the design and operation of accelerators of nuclear particles and electrons. Disparate as these three subjects may appear to be, the trend of physics is rapidly uniting them." [1]

I have two vivid memories of that meeting. The first is being introduced to Robert Oppenheimer by Henrik A. Kramers and discussing with him the effect of radiation reaction on the scattering of an electron in an external field, a subject in which Oppenheimer and Bethe were actively interested at the time.[2] The second is my meeting with Isidor I. Rabi for the first time; he at once fired the question at me: "Do you think the polarization of the vacuum can be measured?" I remember my amazement at a country where experimentalists would know, let alone bother, about vacuum polarization. For this was my first week in the United States. Thus I speak as one of those who, because of age, geography or other reasons did not meet Oppenheimer until after the war. That first week was a preview of things to come.

In January 1947 Oppenheimer gave the Richtmyer Lecture at the New York American Physical Society meeting, on "Creation and Destruction of Mesons." [3] In this lecture he reported on the first results obtained with the 184-inch Berkeley cyclotron. He then went on to discuss the soft component of the cosmic rays, which originates within a few radiation lengths from the top of the atmosphere, and suggested that this component derives from the decay of neutral mesons. Oppenheimer again made this pioneering remark on the role of π^0 mesons in a subsequent paper[4] on multiple-meson production.

After the talk he invited me for a drink in a Broadway bar where he told me that he had been offered the directorship of the Institute for Advanced Study in Princeton. He accepted this post in April, becoming the Institute's third director and the first to hold this position concurrently with a professorship there.

MESONS AND COSMIC RAYS

That spring, I saw Oppenheimer for the first time in full action. Early in 1947 it was suggested from various sides that a number of small panel conferences be held in the various branches of science. Their purpose should be to review recent developments and discuss possible avenues of progress. Under the auspices of the National Academy of Sciences, and with the support of the Rockefeller Foundation, the first such conference in physics took place from June 2 to 4, 1947, on Shelter Island. For this meeting Oppenheimer wrote the outline of topics for discussion, "The Foundations of Quantum Mechanics." As was to happen so often in the years following, he showed himself to be a threefold master: by stressing where the important problems lay, by directing the discussion, and by summarizing the findings.

In his outline he discussed the copiousness of meson production in cosmic radiation in terms of meson theories then current and concluded that "no reasonable formulation along this line will satisfactorily account for the smallness of the subsequent interaction of mesons with nuclear matter." [5] In the discussion of this point, Robert E. Marshak got up to propose that there should be two kinds of mesons.[6] It was, you may recall, in September of that year that Cecil F. Powell reported the discovery of pi–mu decay at a Copenhagen conference.

The Shelter Island conference witnessed the opening of a new chapter in quantum electrodynamics. Two of the men who played a leading role in this development were associated with Oppenheimer in the Berkeley days. One of them, Willis Lamb (Berkeley Ph.D. 1938, under Oppenheimer), gave an account of the early results of the Lamb-Retherford experiment,[7] which indicated an upward shift of about 1000 me for the $2^2S_{\frac{1}{2}}$ state of hydrogen as compared with the prediction for a single particle in a Coulomb field. Rabi reported [8] on a deviation in the hyperfine structure of hydrogen and deuterium which was soon to be attributed by Julian Schwinger (Oppenheimer's research associate at Berkeley 1940–1941) to an anomaly of the magnetic moment of the electron.

Oppenheimer immediately emphasized that here one might have to do with self-energy effects. Small wonder. In 1930 he had already been concerned with atomic level displacements due to radiative effects.[9] In 1934, Dirac[10] and, independently, Furry and Oppenheimer[11] had noted "that the charge of the electron defined in the usual way is not the true charge" (charge renormalization) and that there should be deviations from Coulomb's law, a point taken up further by Edwin A. Uehling and by Serber. Here, too, was the answer to the problem Rabi had posed a few months before: whatever one was measuring, it was not exclusively the "Uehling terms" because these by themselves give an effect which is much too small and of the wrong sign. As is known, the electromagnetic nature of the Lamb shift became evident soon after the conference.[12]

AT THE INSTITUTE

In the late summer of 1947 Oppenheimer and his family moved to Princeton and a new era began at the Institute for Advanced Study.

Physics had been represented at the Institute since its inception—the first two professors to be appointed in 1933 were Oswald Veblen and Albert Einstein. Bohr and Dirac had been frequent visitors and Pauli spent the war years there. In addition, a score of other physicists had worked at the Institute at one time or another. Upon Oppenheimer's arrival, though, a function and quality of the Institute developed which for reasons to be profoundly respected had not been there before. It became a center for physics.

Once again Oppenheimer's outstanding talent for assembling the right people and stimulating them to great effort was the decisive factor. Regular periods of residence for eminent physicists have continued to play an important role in the life of the Institute. But from the very start, Oppenheimer brought to physics at the Institute a new emphasis on youth. In fact, on his arrival in Princeton, five research associates from Berkeley came with him as the first temporary physics members in the new style. The first physics paper to come out of the Institute after he took over is an application of mass renormalization by one of these associates.[13] It deals with the same problem that was mentioned earlier on which Oppenheimer had worked in collaboration with Bethe. This is characteristic of the continuity as well as for the transition in Oppenheimer's activities. For from then on, his principal activity was not so much his own research. Rather it was to be, in the original meaning, a director of physics.

A director, rather than a teacher in the conventional sense, for there is no such teaching at the Institute. We had our seminars, to be sure. They were lively—sometimes very lively

—and Oppenheimer's sharp insights played a major part in making them so. Yet Oppenheimer's main contribution to the work and the style of the Institute was not merely the conducting of a seminar. His influence was far more important, more subtle perhaps, but no less inspiriting. He could convey to young men a sense of the extraordinary relevance of the physics of their day and give them a sense of their participation in a great adventure, as for example in the Richtmyer Lecture: "There are rich days ahead for physics; we may hope, I think, to be living in one of the heroic ages of physical science, where, as in the past, a vast new field of experience has taught us its new lessons and its new order." [14] He could define, and thereby enhance, their dedication, by words such as these: "People who practice science, who try to learn, believe that knowledge is good. They have a sense of guilt when they do not try to acquire it. This keeps them busy. . . . It seems hard to live any other way than thinking that it was better to know something than not to know it; and that the more you know the better, provided you know it honestly." [15] To an unusual degree, Oppenheimer possessed the ability to instill such attitudes in the young physicists around him, to urge them not to let up. He could be critical, sharply critical at times, of their efforts, but there was no greater satisfaction for him than to see such efforts bear fruit and then to tell others of the good work that someone had done.

Oppenheimer supplied much impetus to the two sequels to the Shelter Island conference. At the first, the Pocono Manor Inn conference (March 30–April 1, 1948), at which Schwinger gave an eight-hour marathon talk, Richard P. Feynman's contribution to quantum electrodynamics was not yet fully appreciated. At the very time of this conference, on April 2, Sin-Itiro Tomonaga sat down in Tokyo and wrote an important letter to Oppenheimer in which he gave an account of the independent progress that had been made by him and other

Japanese physicists toward a "self-consistent subtraction method," or as we now say, the renormalization method. The Old Stone on the Hudson meeting, April 11–14, 1949, also had experimental and theoretical refinements of electrodynamics as a main theme, and at that time Feynman's diagrams were understood. This was the third and last of the precursors of the Rochester conferences.*

Meanwhile, in the years of which I now speak, the late forties and early fifties, Oppenheimer had become widely known as a principal representative figure in the field of the natural sciences. Thus in 1948 when the American Institute of Physics inaugurated a new journal, *Physics Today*, the dialogue between theory and experiment was symbolized on the cover of its first issue by a picture of a porkpie sombrero tossed on a cyclotron. And when in 1950 the *Scientific American* devoted an issue to a summary of that incredibly full half-century in science, 1900–1950, it was fitting that Oppenheimer should write the general introduction.[16]

In this introduction, Oppenheimer for once talked about himself, something he did only rarely. All those whose lives have been enriched for having known his warmth and his friendship, as has mine, had to know Robert's uncommonly strong protective sense of privacy, which was sometimes mistaken for an inner aloofness. In any event, in the introduction just mentioned, he told how, twenty years earlier, Dirac had taken him "to task with characteristic gentleness. I understand [Dirac had said] that you are writing poetry as well as working at physics. I do not see how you can do both. In science one says something that no one knew before in a way that everybody can understand. Whereas in poetry . . ."

---

* These are the most important of the international conferences on high energy physics. Begun in 1951, they are now biannual. Even if held elsewhere, they are still known as "Rochester Conferences."

POET AND PHYSICIST

Oppenheimer's physics papers were the real stuff, no poetry there. Yet—as is familiar to all who knew him, and as can also clearly be seen in his more reflective writings—it is an integral part of the Oppenheimer style that he had more than a touch of the poet. He was a master of the language.

For many of us it was a joy to hear him discuss or paraphrase a subject, especially if it was somewhat familiar, for Oppenheimer's discourse was not for beginners. But to some his style was alien. It is too simple to say that Oppenheimer polarized his surroundings, but it is true that the reactions he evoked were never bland.

SECURITY

I must now briefly but sharply interrupt the main line of this account in order to make mention of events which have affected all of us, though not all of us equally.

On Sunday, April 11, 1954, a major newspaper ran an article the title of which read, in part: "Next Target: the Leading Physicists." It was the first intimation to the world at large of a coming ordeal that had long been expected and that would be in the public domain the very next day. I shall now relate something of the impact of these tense months on life at the Institute.

The Institute as such has never been asked to accept nor has it ever sought a classified contract.[17] Clearly, therefore, the tumult of those days did not affect the nature of the work done there. It is equally clear that these happenings dampened the spirit at the Institute even more than they did at many other centers. On April 14, Herbert Maass, chairman of the Board of Trustees, announced that Oppenheimer would continue as director. Yet there was reason for uncertainty

37

about this, because the directorship of the Institute is an appointment that needs a formal vote of renewal by the Trustees each year. Fortunately, this concern turned out to be unfounded.

Before the final decision, the council of the American Physical Society issued a statement on June 13 through its president, Hans A. Bethe, in which it was stressed that the turn of events might "prevent the development of the best thought." After the final ruling had been made, a formal statement was issued by all twenty-six permanent members and professors emeriti at the Institute. It read, in part:

"Dr. Oppenheimer has performed for this country services of another kind, more indirect and less conspicuous but nevertheless, we believe, of great significance. For seven years now he has with inspired devotion directed the work at the Institute for Advanced Study, for which he has proved himself singularly well suited by the unique combination of his personality, his broad scientific interests and his acute scholarship. We are proud to give public expression at this time to our loyal appreciation of the many benefits that we all derive from our association with him in this capacity." *

While I speak as one of the many who think at this moment of a man treated with gross injustice, as one of the many who deeply respect the stand of Harry Smyth,† even so this is not the time to relive our own anguish. Let us rather

* This statement was signed by: James W. Alexander, Julian H. Bigelow, Harold F. Cherniss, Freeman J. Dyson, Albert Einstein, Kurt Gödel, Hetty Goldman, Herman H. Goldstine, Ernst Kantorowicz, E. A. Lowe, Benjamin D. Meritt, Deane Montgomery, Marston Morse, Abraham Pais, Erwin Panofsky, George Placzek, Atle Selberg, Walter W. Stewart, Homer A. Thompson, Oswald Veblen, John von Neumann, Kurt Weitzmann, Herman Weyl, Hassler Whitney, E. L. Woodward, Chen Ning Yang.

† Dr. Henry De Wolf Smyth, the senior member of the Atomic Energy Commission, was the one member of the Commission who voted in favor of reinstating Oppenheimer's access to secret Government information.

remember that in spite of other serious responsibilities, which had to be part of his destiny, Oppenheimer's foremost devotion was to physics. As he put it himself sometime later: "We have, all of us, to preserve our competence in our own professions, to preserve what we know intimately, to preserve our mastery. This is, in fact, our only anchor in honesty." [18] For this reason, it was a comfort to him that physics flourished at the Institute during these years.

In some old notes from the Pocono conference I found these comments. By Oppenheimer: "Now it doesn't matter that things are infinite." By Rabi: "What the hell should I measure now?" They reflect the sense of optimism of the late forties, especially the expectation that with the new theoretical tools interactions other than electromagnetic ones would soon give sensible results.

The mood and the scene changed drastically in the fifties. It was soon clear that hadrodynamics would not yield as readily to the degree that electrodynamics had. At the same time, a whole new world of particles and interactions began to unfold. I do not recall any mention at Pocono or Old Stone of the original cosmic-ray findings of George D. Rochester and Clifford C. Butler. But it was not long before vast efforts began to develop to penetrate the subnuclear world by the experimentalists with the newly available accelerators and by theoretical physicists who attempted to find new rules, if not laws, to cope with the extended vista of strong, electromagnetic and weak interactions.

So in the fifties we witnessed two main theoretical approach marches. First, the development of a much needed new phenomenology; second, a reconsideration of the foundations of field theory and a search for new methods to cope with situations in which, if not field theory, then at least power series expansions appear to fail.

It is in this period that theoretical particle physics became largely separate from theoretical nuclear physics. The pioneering developments in this new field are most closely associated with work done at the Institute in the Oppenheimer era. Other subjects such as astrophysics and statistical mechanics were also successfully pursued. In those years the Institute became a leading center where aspiring theorists sought to spend time. Its list of alumni is most impressive; they can be found all over this country as well as abroad. All of us who were part of these active, and on the whole harmonious, years will forever be deeply grateful to Robert Oppenheimer.

In the early sixties there was a large scattering of the physics staff at the Institute. Once again Oppenheimer directed the formation of a new team and, by and by, the continuity of the operation will be evident. It was also in this period that the Institute's beautiful new library was opened. When you visit it, you should remember that this is Robert's building. It took some doing to get it done.

SCIENCE AND THE INTELLECTUAL COMMUNITY

In the post-war period Oppenheimer's own writings focused more and more on the fact that the relations between the modern sciences and the general culture of our time are not as intimate and fruitful today as they could be. What precisely was his concern in this matter? Was it the problem of "mass culture"? Of course he recognized the importance of popularization, yet "That is not now my problem," he said.[19] What really preoccupied him was that the span of things the intelligent man can cope with is dangerously narrowing; that the relationships between common sense and specialized knowledge are more tenuous now than ever, because the rate of increase of that which is known is now greater than ever.

Even the scientist often finds it hard to appreciate the essentials of a neighboring discipline, not completely foreign but not quite his own. "Even in physics we do not entirely succeed in spite of a passion for unity which is quite strong." [20]

Was it then his intent to explain isotopic spin to philosophers? No harm in trying, he thought, but "as for particle physics, what we are sure of today may not yet be ready to make its contribution to the common culture." [21]

Briefly, then, what Oppenheimer had in mind was this. First, he addressed himself to what is loosely called the intellectual community. It was primarily within this community that he wished to foster a common understanding. Second, as an example of what in his opinion could profitably be shared, he mentions the lesson of quantum theory called complementarity. This he wished and in fact tried to explain to the biologist, the statesman, and the artist, because he believed that what to the physicist is a technique represents at the same time a general way of thinking that could be liberating to all. Third, he saw a twofold duty for our educational system. In the face of the exploding demands on education we should continue to stress that the cultural life of science lies almost entirely in the intimate view of the professional. At the same time, "No man should escape our universities without . . . some sense of the fact that not through his fault, but in the nature of things, he is going to be an ignorant man, and so is everyone else." [22]

Of the great effort needed to achieve these aims he said the following: "I think that, with the growing wealth of the world, and the possibility that it will not all be used to make new committees, there may indeed be genuine leisure, and that a high commitment on this leisure is that we reknit the discourse and the understanding between the members of our community.

"As a start, we must learn again, without contempt and with great patience, to talk to one another; and we must hear." [23]

Oppenheimer himself talked and wrote with authority on these subjects, science and the intellectual community, an authority that derived from the only primary source acceptable to us: the personal participation of the professional in his craft, whatever the craft may be. Thus it was in keeping with Oppenheimer's style that, as he devoted himself to these general themes, it was never at the expense of his own hard-boiled interests in the progress of physics. He kept fully abreast of all new developments in his field which he loved so deeply.

In early 1966 it became clear that Oppenheimer was most seriously ill. Even then he did not lose his inexhaustible curiosity in physics but kept talking shop, in pain but lucidly, till the end.

Freeman J. Dyson has told me of Oppenheimer's last visit to the Institute. He came to participate in a discussion on the selection of the young physicists who would be members of the Institute during the coming academic year. He knew he would not be there to greet them.

Robert Oppenheimer died on February 18, 1967.

Any single one of the following contributions would have marked Oppenheimer out as a pre-eminent scientist: his own research work in physics; his influence as a teacher; his leadership at Los Alamos; the growth of the Institute for Advanced Study as a leading center of theoretical physics under his directorship; and his efforts to promote a more common understanding of science. When all is combined, we honor Oppenheimer as a great leader of science. When all is interwoven with the dramatic events that centered around him, we remember Oppenheimer as one of the most remarkable personalities of this century. In the years to come the physicist will speak of him. So will the historian and the psychologist, the playwright and the poet. But it would take the singular combination of talents of this extraordinary man himself to characterize his life in brief. Perhaps Robert has done just that. I shall conclude with a few lines which he wrote many years ago.[24]

"The wealth and variety of physics itself, the greater wealth of the natural sciences taken as a whole, the more familiar, yet still strange and far wider wealth of the life of the human spirit, enriched by complementary, not at once compatible ways, irreducible one to the other, have a greater harmony. They are the elements of man's sorrow and his splendour, his frailty and his power, his death and his passing, and his undying deeds."

GLENN T. SEABORG

Public Service and
Human Contributions

MUCH HAS BEEN SAID and written about Robert Oppenheimer by the many friends and students with whom he shared his life—his knowledge, wisdom, and the wealth of his personal warmth and wide range of worldly interests. Thus I would like to begin with my personal recollections of him. I was fortunate enough to have known and worked with him over a long period—particularly in the early years of nuclear discovery and development when we shared some of the excitement of that historic time.

THE EARLY DAYS

I first met Robert Oppenheimer when I went to the University of California as a graduate student in chemistry in 1934. Oppie had then just passed his thirtieth birthday and was an associate professor of physics, dividing his time between Berkeley and the California Institute of Technology in Pasadena. I must confess that he made a terrific impact on me— one that I never quite got over in the following thirty-odd years of acquaintance with him. And I have the feeling that his memories of a gangling, young, naïve, would-be nuclear chemist may have continued to color his own view of me long after I pictured myself as having reached a moderate stage of maturity.

I am afraid that I may have manufactured occasions that made it necessary for me to consult with him regarding my research problems. In retrospect I do not see how these problems could have been of great intrinsic interest to him, but I cannot recall any occasion when he was at all unwilling to help. One particularly puzzling riddle that I presented to Oppie— a real one in this case—concerned the results of the irradiation of various elements with fast neutrons in the MeV energy range. I was doing this work in the mid-1930s with David C. Grahame, also a graduate student at that time. The Japanese physicist Seishi Kikuchi and his co-workers had observed in such experiments the production of electrons in the MeV energy range, and they attributed these to some unusual direct interaction of the fast neutrons with orbital electrons. Grahame and I preferred the view that these electrons were the internal conversion products of gamma rays produced in nuclei that had been excited by the inelastic scattering of the neutrons, at that time an unobserved, or at least unproved, process. But this interpretation presented a problem because the experimental results suggested internal conversion coefficients much higher than had generally been observed. I believe that I succeeded in intriguing Oppie with this problem, although the explanation came some time later as a result of the recognition of the role of spin change in slowing down gamma-ray transitions and increasing their internal conversion.

I had one difficulty with Oppie that I imagine was common to all who sought his advice, that is, facing his tendency to answer your question even before you had fully stated it. In this respect, I recall taking great pains in formulating my questions to him in such a way that I could put the main thrust of my thoughts as early as possible into every sentence.

I particularly remember Oppie's role in physics-department seminars. All of us turned to him for explanation of our experiments in nuclear physics, and his electric personality certainly contributed to our fascination and satisfaction with his performance. I remember particularly a seminar in January 1939 when new results of Otto Hahn and Fritz Strassmann on the splitting of uranium with neutrons were excitedly discussed; I do not recall ever seeing Oppie so stimulated and so full of ideas. As it turned out, I was privileged to witness his first encounter with the phenomenon that was to play such an important role in shaping the future course of events in his life.

As Viki Weisskopf wrote, the year 1939 changed many things, and Viki has given an illuminating account of Oppenheimer's marvelous leadership at Los Alamos. Although I spent the war years at the Metallurgical Laboratory at the University of Chicago, my contacts wth Oppenheimer continued. ⌈ He paid me visits on many of his trips to Chicago, and in our discussions he continued to show enduring interest in chemistry, an aspect of his character that has perhaps not been so well known. ⌉ We discussed not only the problems attendant with the chemical purification of plutonium, required for its successful use as an explosive, but also the various chemical methods under investigation for the separation of plutonium from uranium and fission products at Hanford, Washington.

GENERAL ADVISORY COMMITTEE

My closest association with him was at the time I served as a member of the Atomic Energy Commission's General Advisory Committee (GAC) during the first three and one half years of its existence. The GAC played an important role in those formative years of the Commission, and Oppenheimer, as chairman of the GAC, was the architect of that role. The GAC, whose other members at that time were Conant, Du-Bridge, Fermi, Hood Worthington, Rabi, Hartley Rowe, Cyril S. Smith, and Oliver E. Buckley, had the responsibility of setting the initial course of the AEC's military program and guiding the first ventures in the peaceful uses of nuclear energy.

I recall how impressed I was with Oppie's leadership of the committee. During the three and a half years, about twenty sessions of the GAC were held. These three-day-long meetings were usually held over the weekends when we had the time, or took the time, to leave our other duties. At the conclusion of each session, when the AEC commissioners came in to review our work, Oppie presented a masterful summary of the proceedings. This was Oppenheimer at his very best. I regret that tape recordings were not made of these eloquent summations of our deliberations, for these were better than the written record that followed and would provide fascinating historical material.

It is not generally appreciated how much of Oppenheimer's efforts in those early GAC meetings went toward strengthening the Commission's and our nation's position in national defense. He devoted great effort to programs that strengthened the position of the Los Alamos Laboratory, and he emphasized the priority of plutonium production at Hanford.

PEACEFUL USES OF ATOMIC ENERGY

⌠ During those early GAC days Oppie also showed his great desire to foster the peaceful role of the atom. Like most of us he wanted to see the early development of nuclear power. But, also like most of us at that time, he was overly pessimistic about the possibilities of rapid growth in this area. At least, judged by current activity, his early report on the outlook for developing civilian nuclear power did not anticipate the possibilities being realized today.

During his leadership of the GAC, Oppenheimer spearheaded the move for strong AEC support of fundamental research. In no other era of human history had the world seen such a transfer of theory into application as in the events of the Manhattan Project. Perhaps better than any other person, Oppenheimer, who had overseen so much of this project, saw this transfer take place. And to a man of his depth and philosophical insight the realization of the future implications of fundamental research had a most profound effect. He saw the dawn of a new age of science and knew that the government's relationship to science could never be the same. Therefore, he argued brilliantly in GAC proposals to ensure that the AEC would play a leading role in fundamental nuclear research. In one of his statements in support of nuclear research he made what AEC Chairman David Lilienthal termed "as brilliant, lively, and accurate a statement as I believe I have ever heard."

In line with his case for AEC support of fundamental research Oppie advocated that the Commission support such work in the universities and other institutions, thus helping to initiate the incredible growth of science resulting from government-university co-operation.

Finally, regarding Oppenheimer's contributions on the GAC—and I have touched on only a few of them—he was a strong advocate of making fundamental scientific information available to all scientists and of distributing materials such as radioisotopes to scientists abroad, not only for medical investigation and therapy, but for use in basic research.

Oppie's contributions to his government extended far beyond his service during the war and his work on the GAC.

NUCLEAR DETECTION SYSTEM

While still at Los Alamos he was one of the first to recognize that a nuclear-test detection system should be established and so recommended while he was still with the Manhattan District. As chairman of the Committee on Atomic Energy of the Joint Research and Development Board, on a number of occasions he was helpful throughout the years 1948–50 to the program that was conducting research and development on techniques for detecting nuclear explosions. I had the privilege of serving with him on the panel that evaluated and confirmed the report by early scientific-detection experts that the Soviets had, indeed, broken the U.S. monopoly on nuclear weapons by testing a device of their own on August 29, 1949. Serving in a similar capacity, he endorsed the 1951 findings of the U.S. detection system that the Soviets had conducted their second and third nuclear tests.

SERVICE IN MANY CAPACITIES

He served his government in numerous other capacities: in 1945, on Secretary Henry L. Stimson's Scientific Panel of the War Department's Interim Committee; and in 1946 on President Harry S. Truman's Evaluation Committee for Operation Crossroads. He served the Joint Research and Development Board from 1947 to 1952 in many capacities, perhaps the chief of which was as a member and chairman of its Committee on Atomic Energy. He was a member of the Naval Research Advisory Committee from 1949 to 1952 and the Science Advisory Committee, Office of Defense Mobilization, from 1951 to 1954. He served on the Secretary of State's Panel on Disarmament in 1952 and 1953. And this enumeration of his services to his country is only a representative fraction of his total contributions.

We are all familiar with Oppenheimer's leading role in formulating the Acheson-Lilienthal Report of 1946 that called for the creation of an international authority to control all work in atomic energy. Much of the substance of this plan, which emphasized the peaceful potential of atomic energy, was incorporated in the proposal later presented to the United Nations by Bernard Baruch. Although the Baruch proposal was rejected, it set the tone for future thinking in international control and co-operation and anticipated much of what we hope to achieve in the future. Today, our hopes for a nonproliferation treaty owe much to this original groundwork. Oppenheimer's contributions to the Baruch plan were indicative of his farsightedness and depth of understanding as well as his humanitarian outlook.

These are some of the contributions in the area of governmental public service that Robert Oppenheimer rendered to his country. But his public-service contributions went far beyond this. He was tireless in his efforts to explain and interpret science—its meaning, its intellectual, cultural, humane, economic, political and sociological implications—to the broadest possible audience. He did this by means of speeches to a diverse spectrum of audiences, by the written word in a wide range of publications, by participation before congressional committees, by numerous appearances on radio and television, and by active membership in many organizations and societies devoted to this cause.

RECOGNITION OF OPPENHEIMER'S CONTRIBUTION

His many contributions to his country were recognized by three Presidents, who bestowed many honors upon him. First, President Truman awarded him the Medal of Merit in 1946 for his work at Los Alamos. The citation accompanying this award praised Oppenheimer for ". . . his great scientific experience and ability, his inexhaustible energy, his rare capacity as an organizer and executive, his initiative and resourceful-ness, and his unswerving devotion to duty. . . ."

The second President to honor him was John F. Kennedy. This was in the form of an invitation to a White House dinner given in honor of Nobel Prize winners. President Kennedy had also planned to present Oppenheimer with the Fermi Award.

The third presidential honor he received was from Lyndon B. Johnson in 1963. On this occasion the President presented Oppenheimer with the AEC's Enrico Fermi Award. In personally making the award at the White House, President Johnson said in part: "Dr. Oppenheimer, I am pleased that you are here today to receive formal recognition for your many contributions to theoretical physics and to the advancement of science in our nation. Your leadership in the development of an outstanding school of theoretical physics in the United States and your contributions to our basic knowledge make your achievements unique in the scientific world."

OPPENHEIMER'S ROLE AS A TEACHER

It seems to me that President Johnson's inclusion of a reference to Oppenheimer's role as a teacher was singularly appropriate. His role as an extraordinary and almost unique teacher must certainly be included among his public service and human contributions. Robert Oppenheimer will go down in the history of science for his founding of what has been called "the American school of theoretical physics."

Speaking of Oppenheimer's extraordinary talents as a teacher, Bethe wrote in *Science*: "His lectures were a great ex-perience, for experimental as well as theoretical physicists. In addition to a superb literary style, he brought to them a degree of sophistication in physics previously unknown in the United

States. Here was a man who obviously understood all the deep secrets of quantum mechanics and who yet made it clear that the most important questions were unanswered." [1]

When Oppenheimer became director of the Institute for Advanced Study at Princeton in 1947, the physics department of the Institute became the new international mecca of theoretical physics, just as Copenhagen had served this role in the 1920s and 1930s. Pauli, Dirac and Yukawa often came to Princeton during the Oppenheimer era at the Institute, and Murray Gell-Mann, Marvin L. Goldberger, Geoffrey F. Chew, Francis E. Low, Yoichiro Nambu, Dyson, Pais, Tsung Dao Lee and Chen Ning Yang were among the many who worked there under Oppie's inspired leadership.

Although his greatest contribution to science was probably his role as an inspiring teacher, organizer and catalyst of the "new physics," Oppenheimer was a creative scientist who made many significant contributions to theoretical physics.

HIS HUMAN CONTRIBUTION

It is virtually impossible to summarize the additional "human" contributions of Robert Oppenheimer, just as it is almost impossible to separate them from his scientific contributions. Those scientists who knew him well and worked with him closely were equally impressed by the scope of his knowledge and interest—in languages, literature, the arts, music, and the social and political problems of the world—as they were by his scientific wisdom. Above all, those who knew him, read his writings, or heard him speak were impressed by his fervent desire to see and relate an order and purpose in the entire spectrum of human existence and experience.

Oppenheimer was probably unique among scientists of our age in his effect on, and high standing among, other scientists.

His magnetic, really electric, personality, his charismatic presence and his unique style commanded attention in a manner equaled by few scientists. His basically humanitarian outlook and his obvious concern for the over-all welfare of humanity were widely recognized and appreciated throughout the world of science. And these qualities carried over to the world of nonscientists to an extent that was almost without parallel.

The death of Robert Oppenheimer not only marks the passing of an era of physics but also portends an irreplaceable loss to the world of all scientists and nonscientists alike.

Perhaps the best way to show the breadth and depth of his thinking would be to quote from some of his numerous writings and speeches, which exemplify so well his human and humanitarian qualities. The few passages I have chosen represent only a small sampling of his thoughts, but I think they may be significant on this occasion.

Speaking before a Japanese audience at the Bunkyo Public Hall of Tokyo, September 1960, he commented aptly enough on tradition:

"Tradition, of course, is to preserve, to refresh, to transmit, and to increase our insight into what men have done as men, in their art, their learning, their poetry, their religion, their politics, their science, feeling, thinking beings with our experiences, to cope with our sorrows, to limit and make noble our joys, to understand what is happening to us, to talk to one another, to relate one thing to another, to find the great themes which organize our experience and give it meaning. It is what makes us human." [2]

In an address before the Tenth Anniversary Conference of the Congress for Cultural Freedom, in Berlin, June 1960, he again touched on tradition, this time introducing one of his favorite themes—the need for common understanding.

"I have been much concerned that in this world we have

so largely lost the ability to talk with one another. In the great succession of deep discoveries, we have become removed from one another in tradition, and in a certain measure even in language. We have had neither the time nor the skill nor the dedication to tell one another what we have learned, nor to listen nor to hear, nor to welcome its enrichment of the common culture and the common understanding. Thus the public sector of our lives, what we have and hold in common, has suffered as have the illumination of the arts, the deepening of justice, and virtue, the ennobling of power and of our common discourse. We are less men for this. Our specialized traditions flourish; our private beauties thrive; but in those high undertakings where man derives strength and insight from the public excellence, we have been impoverished. We hunger for nobility: the rare words and acts that harmonize simplicity and truth. In this I see some connection with the great unresolved public problems: survival, liberty, fraternity." [3]

In a broadcast talk "Prospects in the Arts and Sciences" for the Columbia University Bicentennial, December 26, 1954, Oppenheimer spoke of the common thread of the arts and sciences. "Both the man of science and the man of art live always at the edge of mystery, surrounded by it, both always, as the measure of their creation, have had to do with harmonization of what is new and what is familiar with the balance between novelty and synthesis, with the struggle to make partial order in total chaos. They can, in their work and in their lives, help themselves, help one another, and help all men. They can make the paths that connect the villages of arts and sciences with each other and with the world at large the multiple, varied, precious bonds of a true and world-wide community." [4]

The theme of "community" was prevalent in many of his talks, as exemplified by this quotation from his address "Science and Our Times," delivered to the Roosevelt University Founders and Friends Dinner in Chicago on May 22, 1956.

"Occasionally between the sciences, and more rarely between a science and other parts of our experience and knowledge, there is a correspondence, an analogy, a partial mapping of two sets of ideas and words. We learn then to translate from one language into another. Ours is thus a united world, united by countless bonds. Everything can be related to anything; everything cannot be related to everything. It may perhaps then be a beginning of wisdom to learn of the virtues, of the restraint and tolerance, and of the sense of fraternity that will be asked of us, if, in this largely new world, we are to live, not in chaos, but in community." [5]

In the same talk he stresses the need for more learning:

"In a free world, if it is to remain free, we must maintain, with our lives if need be, but surely by our lives, the opportunity for a man to learn anything. We need to do more: We need to cherish man's curiosity, his understanding, his love, so that he may indeed learn what is new and hard and deep. We need to do this in a world in which the changes wrought by the applications of science, and the din of communication from remote and different places, complement the unhinging, unmooring effects of the explosive growth in knowledge itself." [6]

For some closing thoughts I turn to the final paragraphs of Robert Oppenheimer's lecture at the University of Wisconsin, May 10, 1959—an address called "The Tree of Knowledge." Here he expresses his belief that though we live in a world of growing specialization we must also grow in our ability to communicate with our fellow man.

"Civilization, all we are, all we know, all we can do, rests on our power to tell each other about things. We do that in more ways than words; but if we do not do that, we are not human. That is why I have been willing to trouble you with an account of what seems to me a very real problem.

"We have a double duty; and I think this has its analogs for everybody. I say it, I cannot help it, as a man who hopes he will spend some part of his life always with physicists and in physics. We have a duty to the things which are necessarily limited, which we are close to and know well and love; they may be a discipline, they may be an art, they may be a community, but they will always have to be fairly small, to have human compass. We have another duty, which is to be open and welcoming to all our fellows who are not part of this community, but are still necessary and beautiful parts of the human community. And this double sense of faithfulness to that which is our own, and openness to all that is human, is perhaps one of the attitudes, which more even than reform in education, more than any political gimmickry, will help to see us through one of the most peculiar episodes in man's history." [7]

REFERENCE NOTES

The Early Years

1. "On the Quantum Theory of Vibration-Rotation Bands," *Proceedings of the Cambridge Philosophical Society,* 23 (1926), 327–335.
2. "On the Quantum Theory of the Problem of Two Bodies," *Proceedings of the Cambridge Philosophical Society,* 23 (1926), 422–431.
3. "On the Quantum Theory of Molecules," *Annalen der Physik,* 84 (1927), 457–484.
4. "Note on the Theory of Interaction of Field and Matter," *Physical Review,* 35 (1930), 461–477.
5. "On the Theory of Electrons and Protons," letter, *Physical Review,* 35 (1930), 562–563.
6. "Relativistic Theory of the Photoelectric Effect. Part II. Photoelectric Absorption of Ultragamma Radiation," *Physical Review,* 38 (1931), 57–79.
7. "On the Production of the Positive Electron," letter, *Physical Review,* 44 (1933), 53–55.
8. "On the Theory of the Electron and Positive," *Physical Review,* 45 (1934), 245–262.
9. "On Multiplicative Showers," *Physical Review,* 51 (1937), 220–231.
10. "Note on the Nature of Cosmic-Ray Particles," letter, *Physical Review,* 51 (1937), 1113.
11. "The Production of Soft Secondaries by Mesotrons," *Physical Review,* 57 (1940), 75–81.
12. "The High Energy Soft Component of Cosmic Rays," abstract, *Physical Review,* 60 (1941), 159.
13. "The Disintegration of Lithium by Protons," abstract, *Physical Review,* 43 (1933), 380.

14. "Note on the Transmutation Function for Deuterons," *Physical Review*, 48 (1935), 500–502.

15. "Note on Resonances in Transmutations of Light Nuclei" (with F. Kalckar and R. Serber), *Physical Review*, 52 (1937), 279–282; "Note on Boron Plus Proton Reactions" (with R. Serber), *ibid.*, 53 (1938), 636–638.

16. "On the Stability of Stellar Neutron Cores" (with R. Serber), letter, *Physical Review*, 54 (1938), 540; "On Massive Neutron Cores" (with G. M. Volkoff), *ibid.*, 55 (1939), 374–381.

17. "On Continued Gravitational Contraction," *Physical Review*, 56 (1939), 455–459.

18. "On the Interaction of Mesotrons and Nuclei," *Physical Review*, 60 (1941), 150–152.

19. W. Pauli, "Die Allgemeinen Prinzipien der Wellenmechanik," *Handbuch der Physik*, 24 (1933).

The Princeton Period

1. *Physical Review*, 70 (1946), 784.

2. H. A. Bethe and J. R. Oppenheimer, *Physical Review*, 70 (1946), 451, 796.

3. J. R. Oppenheimer, *Physical Review*, 71 (1947), 462.

4. H. W. Lewis, J. R. Oppenheimer, and S. A. Wouthuysen, *Physical Review*, 73 (1948), 127.

5. M. Conversi, E. Pancini, and O. Piccioni, *Physical Review*, 71 (1947), 209, 557.

6. The statement that "the particle with mass determined from the range of nuclear forces is the Yukawa particle and not the meson found in cosmic rays" appears first, I believe, in S. Sakata and T. Inoue, *Progress of Theoretical Physics*, 1 (1946), 143. The Shelter Island discussions led to the paper by R. E. Marshak and H. A. Bethe, *Physical Review*, 72 (1947), 506. The Japanese paper did not reach the United States until early 1948; see R. E. Marshak in *Proceedings of the Kyoto Conference*, 1965, p. 180.

7. W. E. Lamb and R. C. Retherford, *Physical Review*, 71 (1947), 241.

8. J. E. Nafe, E. B. Nelson, and I. I. Rabi, *Physical Review*, 71 (1947), 914. See also G. *Breit, Physical Review*, 72 (1947), 784; H. M. Foley and P. Kusch, *ibid.*, 72 (1947), 1256; *ibid.*, 73 (1948), 412; G. Breit, *ibid.*, 74 (1948), 656.

9. J. R. Oppenheimer, *Physical Review*, 35 (1930), 461.

10. P. A. M. Dirac, *Proceedings of the Seventh Solvay Conference*, 1934.

11. W. H. Furry and J. R. Oppenheimer, *Physical Review*, 45 (1934), 245.

12. See H. A. Bethe, *Physical Review*, 72 (1947), 339.

13. H. W. Lewis, *Physical Review*, 73 (1946), 173.

14. From the unpublished manuscript of the Richtmyer Lecture. See Note 3 to this chapter.

15. J. R. Oppenheimer, "Knowledge and the Structure of Culture," The Helen Kenyon Lecture, Vassar College, October 1958.

16. J. R. Oppenheimer, "The Age of Science: 1900–1950," *Scientific American* (September 1950), Vol. 183, No. 3, 20–23.

17. See also the comments by J. R. Oppenheimer in the "Transcript of the Hearings," *In the Matter of J. Robert Oppenheimer*, Washington: U. S. Government Printing Office, 1954, p. 26.

18. J. R. Oppenheimer, "On Science and Culture," *Encounter* (October 1962).

19. *Ibid.*

20. *Ibid.*

21. J. R. Oppenheimer in *Perspectives of Modern Physics*, Essays in Honor of H. A. Bethe, New York: Interscience Publishing Co., 1966.

22. J. R. Oppenheimer, "Science, Values and the Human Community," Fulbright Conference on Higher Education, Sarah Lawrence College, June 1957.

23. J. R. Oppenheimer, "On Science and Culture," *op. cit.*

24. J. R. Oppenheimer, "Science and the Common Understanding," in *The BBC Reith Lectures*, London: Oxford University Press, 1954, p. 91.

Public Service and Human Contributions

1. H. A. Bethe, "Oppenheimer: Where He Was There Was Always Life and Excitement," *Science*, 155 (March 3, 1967), 1080–1084.
2. "The Future of Civilization in the Scientific Age," *France-Aise*, 17 (1961).
3. "A Time of Sorrow and Renewal," *Encounter* (February 1961), Vol. 16, No. 2, 70.
4. Published in *Bulletin of the Atomic Scientists*, 11 (February 1955) 42–44.
5. Published in *Bulletin of the Atomic Scientists*, 12 (September 1956), 235–237.
6. *Ibid.*
7. Unpublished manuscript.

BIOGRAPHICAL NOTES

ANDERSON, CARL DAVID (1905–   ), American physicist

BETHE, HANS ALBRECHT (1906–   ), German-American physicist

BLOCH, FELIX (1905–   ), Swiss-American physicist

BOHR, AAGE NIELS (1922–   ), Danish physicist

BOHR, NIELS (1885–1962), Danish physicist

BORN, MAX (1882–   ), German physicist

BUCKLEY, OLIVER ELLSWORTH (1887–   ), American physicist

BUTLER, CLIFFORD CHARLES (1922–   ), English physicist

CHAO, SHIH CHIEH (1921–   ), Chinese-American physicist

CHEW, GEOFFREY FOUCAR (1924–   ), American physicist

CHRISTY, ROBERT FREDERICK (1916–   ), Canadian-American physicist

COMPTON, ARTHUR HOLLY (1892–   ), American physicist

COMPTON, KARL TAYLOR (1887–1954), American physicist

CONANT, JAMES BRYANT (1893–   ), American chemist

DIRAC, PAUL ADRIEN MAURICE (1902–   ), English physicist

DU BRIDGE, LEE ALVIN (1901–   ), American physicist

DYSON, FREEMAN JOHN (1923–   ), English-American physicist

EINSTEIN, ALBERT (1879–1955), German-American physicist

ELSASSER, WALTER (1904–   ), German-American physicist

FERMI, ENRICO (1901–1954), Italian-American physicist

FEYNMAN, RICHARD PHILLIPS (1918–   ), American physicist

FOWLER, WILLIAM ALFRED (1911–   ), American physicist

FURRY, WENDELL HINKLE (1907–   ), American physicist

GAMOW, GEORGE (1904–1968), Russian-American physicist

GELL-MANN, MURRAY (1929–   ), American physicist

GOLDBERGER, MARVIN LEONARD (1922–   ), American physicist

GRAHAME, DAVID C. (1912–1958), American chemist

GROVES, LESLIE RICHARD (1896–   ), General, Ret., U.S. Army

HAHN, OTTO (1879–1968), German chemist

HALL, HARVEY (1904–   ), American physicist

HEISENBERG, WERNER (1901–   ), German physicist

HENDERSON, MALCOLM COLBY (1904–   ), American physicist

JESSE, WILLIAM POLK (1891–   ), American physicist

KIKUCHI, SEISHI (1902–   ), Japanese physicist

KRAMERS, HENRIK A. (1894–1952), Dutch physicist

KUSAKA, SIUCHI (1915–1947), Japanese-American physicist

LAMB, WILLIS EUGENE, JR. (1913–   ), American physicist

LAURITSEN, CHARLES CHRISTIAN (1892–1968), Danish-American physicist

LAURITSEN, THOMAS (1915–   ), Danish-American physicist

LAWRENCE, ERNEST ORLANDO (1901–1958), American physicist

LEE, TSUNG DAO (1926–   ), Chinese-American physicist

LILIENTHAL, DAVID ELI (1899–   ), American government official; chairman, Atomic Energy Commission (1946–1950)

LOW, FRANCIS EUGENE (1921–   ), American physicist

MC MILLAN, EDWIN MATTISON (1907–   ), American physicist

MARSHAK, ROBERT EUGENE (1916–   ), American physicist and astrophysicist

MICHELSON, ALBERT ABRAHAM (1851–1931), American physicist

MILLIKAN, ROBERT ANDREWS (1858–1953), American physicist

NAMBU, YOICHIRO (1921–   ), Japanese-American physicist

NEDDERMEYER, SETH HENRY (1907–   ), American physicist

NORDSIECK, ARNOLD THEODORE (1911–   ), American physicist

PAULI, WOLFGANG (1900–1958), Austrian-American physicist

PEIERLS, RUDOLF ERNST (1907–   ), English physicist

PENNEY, WILLIAM (1909–   ), English physicist

PHILLIPS, MELBA (1907–   ), American physicist

PLACZEK, GEORGE (1905–   ), Czech-American physicist

PLESSET, MILTON SPINOZA (1908–   ), American physicist

POWELL, CECIL FRANK (1903–   ), English physicist

PUPIN, MICHAEL IDVORSKY (1858–1935), Yugoslavian-American physicist

ROCHESTER, GEORGE DIXON (1908–   ), English physicist

ROWE, HARTLEY (1882–1966), American physicist

ROWLAND, HENRY AUGUSTUS (1848–1903), American physicist

SCHEIN, MARCEL (1902–   ), Czech-American physicist

SCHIFF, LEONARD ISAAC (1929–   ), American physicist

SCHRÖDINGER, ERWIN (1887–1961), Austrian physicist

SCHWINGER, JULIAN (1918–   ), American physicist

SMITH, CYRIL S. (1903–   ), English-American physical
metallurgist

SMYTH, HENRY DE WOLF (1898–   ), American physicist

SNYDER, HARTLAND (1913–   ), American physicist

STEVENSON, EDWARD C. (1907–   ), American physicist

STRASSMANN, FRITZ (1902–   ), German chemist

STREET, JABEZ C. (1906–   ), American physicist

THOMSON, SIR JOSEPH JOHN (1856–1940), English physicist

THORNTON, ROBERT LYSTER (1908–   ), English-American
physicist

TOMONAGA, SIN-ITIRO (1906-   ), Japanese physicist

UEHLING, EDWIN ALBRECHT (1901–   ), American physicist

UREY, HAROLD CLAYTON (1893–   ), American chemist

VAN VLECK, JOHN HASBROUCK (1899–   ), American physicist

VEBLEN, OSWALD (1880–1960), American mathematician

WENTZEL, GREGOR (1898–   ), German-American physicist

WOLLAN, ERNEST OMAR (1902–   ), American physicist

WORTHINGTON, HOOD (1903-   ), American nuclear engineer

YANG, CHEN NING (1927–   ), Chinese-American physicist

YUKAWA, HIDEKI (1907–   ), Japanese physicist

GLOSSARY

ABSORPTION COEFFICIENT. A measure of the ability of a substance to absorb radiation or particles.

BARRIER PENETRATION. In classical physics, a particle situated on one side of a barrier cannot appear on the other side unless it acquires sufficient energy to carry it over the top, just as, in ordinary life, a ball lying next to a wall will not appear on the other side unless it is thrown there. In quantum physics, however, even without enough energy for it to go over the barrier, there is a small probability that the particle will appear on the other side. Barrier penetration plays a fundamental role in RADIOACTIVE DECAY.

CHARGE RENORMALIZATION. The charge of a "bare" particle is that which it would have if it did not interact with fields it itself generates. The charge of the "clothed" particle, the charge actually measured, includes interactions with fields. The correction is known as charge renormalization.

COMPLEMENTARITY. Some things that are usually regarded as purely of a wave character, such as radiation, have particle-like aspects (see GAMMA RAYS). Others, such as electrons, usually regarded as particles, have wave aspects (see WAVE FUNCTION). The wave and particle aspects are two complementary views of an entity. A single experiment will reveal one or the other aspect, but not both.

DIRAC EQUATION. A mathematical description of the behavior of the electron and a number of other particles. It is an extension of the original formulation of QUANTUM MECHANICS to include the theory of relativity. The Dirac equation predicted anti-particles.

ELECTRON-POSITRON SHOWERS. A very high-energy photon (synonymous with GAMMA RAY) gives rise to PAIR PRODUCTION. Near a nucleus, the electron and positron will each radiate photons (of lower energy than the original), some of which, in turn, will produce additional electron-positron pairs; these, in their turn, will radiate additional photons, and so on. The photons and pairs travel mainly in the same direction, and the concentration of pairs is called a shower.

EXCHANGE EFFECTS. Purely quantum mechanical effects, having no classical analogue. They arise in interactions between identical particles and stem from the indistinguishability of the particles.

FAST NEUTRONS. Neutrons with considerable energy, roughly, more than 10,000 electron volts to well on in the MEV ENERGY RANGE.

FIELD EMISSION. The emission of electrons from a metal, induced by a very strong electric field.

FIELD THEORY. In order to explain how bodies could interact without direct contact, it was postulated that the presence of the bodies alters all of space, so that other bodies experience a force. This property of space is called a field. In modern field theory, fields are associated with particles. Forces between particles are due to interactions of the particles with fields. For example, the force between two charged particles is due to the emission by one and the absorption by the other of "units" of the electromagnetic field, quanta of electromagnetic radiation.

FINE STRUCTURE SPLITTING. The splitting of what, upon coarse examination, appears to be a single line in the spectrum of an atom, arising from the interaction between the SPIN of an atomic electron and its motion with respect to the nucleus. If one were to imagine the atom to resemble the solar system, the nucleus corresponding to the sun and the atomic electrons to the planets, then, when an electron's rotation about its own axis (spin) is in the same direction as its revolution

72

about the nucleus, both clockwise for example, the electron will have a slightly different energy from when its spin is opposite to its motion about the nucleus. The energy of motion about the nucleus will be split to correspond to the two cases, giving rise to two lines, closely spaced, in the spectrum.

FISSION PRODUCTS. See NUCLEAR FISSION.

GAMMA RAYS. Quanta, or bundles, of electromagnetic radiation, similar to X rays or light but with higher energy. They have great penetrating power. They are often emitted by radioactive nuclei.

GAUGE INVARIANCE. In classical physics potential energy, the energy associated with position, is relative. When one stands on a chair, one's potential energy can be expressed with respect to the floor, the ceiling, or the center of the earth. Only differences in potential energy are meaningful. The difference in potential energy between standing on the chair and standing on the floor will be the same no matter what the potential energy is expressed relative to. In classical and QUANTUM ELECTRODYNAMICS there is even greater arbitrariness associated with the choice of electromagnetic potential. The choice of electromagnetic potential is referred to as the gauge, and the laws of physics are independent of the gauge, that is, they are gauge invariant.

INELASTIC SCATTERING. Collisions from which the impinging particle emerges with less energy than it had before colliding, having transferred some of its energy to internal energy of the target, causing the latter to vibrate or rotate, for example.

INTERNAL CONVERSION. On occasion, from the nucleus of an atom that emits GAMMA RAYS, an electron will emerge instead of the gamma. This can be regarded roughly as a process in which the gamma, on its way out of the atom, hits an electron in one of the atomic orbits, transferring its energy to the electron so that the electron comes out instead.

IONIZATION LOSSES. When a charged particle passes through

matter, it will knock electrons out of the atoms in its path, a process known as ionization. To knock electrons out of the atoms, energy is required; this energy is supplied by the charged particle, with a consequent loss of some of its original energy.

ISOTOPIC SPIN. Characterization of particles that differ only in electromagnetic properties as different states of a single particle. For example, the neutron and the proton are different states of the NUCLEON.

ISOTOPIC SPIN SELECTION RULES. Only those processes can occur that obey conservation laws, conservation of energy or of angular momentum, for instance. Selection rules specify which processes can and which cannot occur. Isotopic spin selection rules are restrictions imposed by conservation of ISOTOPIC SPIN.

K-EDGE. In studying how the absorption of a substance changes as the wavelength of the incident radiation is varied, it is found that there is a sharp drop in absorption at certain wavelengths. The drop occurs when the energy of the radiation (inversely related to the wavelength) becomes too small to eject an electron from one of the orbits of the atoms that compose the substance, and so the radiation is not absorbed by the atoms. The wavelength at which a drop occurs is called an absorption edge. The K-edge is the wavelength of X rays that corresponds to an energy just too low to eject an electron from the K shell, that is, the innermost orbit. (See PHOTOEFFECT.)

KNOCK-ON ELECTRON. An electron ejected with high energy from an atom by an incident particle of high energy.

MASS ABSORPTION LAW. In passing through a material, radiation (or particles) is absorbed in amounts that depend upon the character of the radiation (or particles) and the type and thickness of material. Sometimes it is more convenient to consider the mass per unit area of material instead of the thickness, the two being related through the density of the material. The expression governing the amount of radiation absorbed in terms of the mass per unit area is the mass absorption law.

MESONS. The word meson was constructed from the Greek word *mesos*, meaning middle, because, when first discovered, the meson was the middleweight particle, its mass between that of the electron and that of the proton. In recent years other mesons have been discovered, some heavier than protons. Mesons play the role in nuclear forces that quanta of electromagnetic radiation play in electric forces. (See FIELD THEORY.)

MESON THEORY. Theory that attributes the interaction between two NUCLEONS to the exchange of MESONS between them. It is one example of FIELD THEORY.

ME V ENERGY RANGE. If two metal plates were connected to a one volt battery, an electron traveling from one plate to the other would acquire an amount of energy equal to one electron volt (eV). One MeV is one million electron volts.

NEUTRON STAR. A star in a very late stage of evolution, it is extremely small—a few miles in diameter—and fantastically dense, the latter quality arising from its being composed of neutrons rather than atoms. If one were to make an analogy between atoms and planetary systems, a neutron star would correspond to a cosmos in which planets were stripped from stars and the stars were pushed together. A cube with dimensions of about a city block, taken from a neutron star, would weigh as much as the earth.

NONORTHOGONAL STATES. A mathematical term. Two states are orthogonal if the vector (arrow) representing one state is perpendicular to that of the other. They are nonorthogonal if the vectors are not perpendicular.

NUCLEAR FISSION. The splitting of a heavy nucleus into two or more fragments (fission products) of comparable mass, plus several neutrons. Considerable energy is released in the process, which can occur spontaneously or be induced by a neutron. The number of neutrons increasing with each fission, the process can lead to the chain reaction utilized in the atomic bomb.

NUCLEON ISOBARS. A nucleon is a proton or a neutron, the two being the constituents of the nucleus of an atom. A nucleon isobar is an excited state of the nucleon, that is, a state in which the nucleon has more energy than it normally has.

OPACITIES. A term that pertains to the likelihood of absorption of electromagnetic radiation by materials (usually stellar), that is their opaqueness.

PAIR PRODUCTION. A GAMMA RAY with an energy greater than one MeV can, in the neighborhood of another particle, transform itself into an electron and a positron, the two constituting a pair. The process is called pair production. One MeV is the minimum energy for the process, for ½ MeV is the energy that corresponds to the mass of the electron, and of the positron.

PHOTOEFFECT. When electromagnetic radiation such as light or X rays is incident on a material, it can eject an electron from an atom of the material. If the radiation disappears in the process, the process is called the photoelectric effect, or photoeffect. (See K-EDGE).

PLUTONIUM. An artificially produced metallic element comprising several RADIOISOTOPES. The plutonium nucleus contains 94 protons, 92 being the maximum number in a substance occurring naturally (in uranium).

QUANTUM ELECTRODYNAMICS. Deals with interactions of charged systems with electromagnetic fields when the systems are of atomic dimensions. The interaction between two electrons, for example, occurs through the emission of a quantum of electromagnetic radiation by one and its absorption by the other. Quantum electrodynamics is a branch of quantum FIELD THEORY and is perhaps the most successful theory in all of science in terms of the range and precision of its predictions.

QUANTUM MECHANICS. The term is used interchangeably with QUANTUM THEORY today.

QUANTUM THEORY. The departure from Newton's classical mechanics initiated in 1900 by Max Planck, which stated, among other things, that atoms emit and absorb energy in discrete units (quanta) of electromagnetic radiation. One mathematical formulation of the theory is given by the SCHRÖDINGER EQUATION. Predictions of quantum theory differ quantitatively from those of Newtonian theory only for systems of atomic dimensions. They differ qualitatively, however, in that they are not absolute; instead, they give the probability of obtaining a particular outcome in a particular measurement.

RADIATIVE CORRECTIONS. When two particles interact there is an exchange of radiation (or particles) between them. In addition to this main interaction, such processes as the following might occur: particle A might emit radiation, then emit some more radiation that reaches particle B; then A might reabsorb the radiation it emitted before that which reached B. The "side" emissions and absorptions that are not the direct primary interaction constitute some of the radiative corrections.

RADIOACTIVE DECAY. The spontaneous emission of particles or electromagnetic radiation by the nuclei of certain atoms.

RADIOISOTOPES. If the atoms of two substances have the same number of protons in their nuclei, but not the same number of neutrons, the substances are isotopes and have almost identical chemical properties. If an isotope is radioactive, it is a radioisotope.

ROCHESTER CONFERENCES. A series of conferences on high-energy physics. These were first held in Rochester New York, and they are still called Rochester Conferences even when held elsewhere.

SCHRÖDINGER EQUATION. The counterpart in QUANTUM MECHANICS of Newton's equation, force equals mass times acceleration, in classical mechanics. The Schrödinger equation can be used to predict the properties of systems like atoms.

SELF ENERGY. The energy a particle has owing to its interaction with the field it itself generates.

SPIN. This can be regarded, crudely, as a particle's rotation about its own axis, similar to the rotation of the earth about its axis.

SPIN CHANGE. A change in direction of the SPIN of a particle. Roughly, if a particle were rotating about its axis in a clockwise direction and then suddenly began rotating in a counterclockwise direction, that would constitute a spin change.

STATISTICS. In this context, statistics relates to the classifying of different kinds of particles into two groups, one (obeying Fermi-Dirac statistics) in which no two particles of the same kind, for instance, electrons, can be "doing exactly the same thing," and the other (obeying Bose-Einstein statistics) in which no such restrictions are imposed.

STRONG COUPLING THEORY. Theory that attributes the interaction between two NUCLEONS is to the exchange of any number of MESONS (in contrast to weak coupling, which assumes that a description in terms of one meson is adequate).

THOMSON FORMULA. A mathematical expression governing the scattering of electromagnetic radiation by free electron (one not attached to an atom).

VACUUM POLARIZATION. According to predictions of the DIRAC EQUATION, a vacuum is not emptiness, nothingness, but is a sea of positive and negative charges in equal numbers so that they neutralize each other and appear not to be present. When a particle (or radiation) is introduced, however, it produces a redistribution of the charges in the vacuum, or a polarization of the vacuum. (The redistribution occurs through PAIR PRODUCTION and the almost instantaneous annihilation of the pairs.)

WAVE FUNCTION. A mathematical expression the value of which depends upon the point in space being considered. It is obtained from the SCHRÖDINGER or the DIRAC EQUATION. The wave function enables one to predict the outcome of any experiment, including the probability of a particle's being found at a particular point.

CHRONOLOGY

1904   J. R. Oppenheimer born April 22, in New York City

1925   B.A. from Harvard College, *summa cum laude*

1926   Studies under Ernest Rutherford at the Cavendish Laboratory, Cambridge University

1927   Receives his Ph.D. under Max Born at the University of Göttingen

1928   National Research Fellow at Harvard University and at the California Institute of Technology

1929   Fellow of the International Education Board with Wolfgang Pauli at the University of Leyden and Zurich

1929   Joint appointment at the University of California at Berkeley and California Institute of Technology

1936   Full professor at Berkeley and California Institute of Technology

1940   Marries Katherine Harrison

1941   Is elected to the United States National Academy of Sciences

1942   Organizes the Los Alamos Scientific Laboratory

1943   Is appointed director of the Los Alamos Scientific Laboratory

1946   Receives the United States Medal for Merit
              Helps prepare the Atomic Energy Act of 1946

1946–52   Chairman of the General Advisory Committee of the United States Atomic Energy Commission

1946–66   Director of the Institute for Advanced Study at Princeton, New Jersey

1948   President of the American Physical Society

1954   Is investigated by the Personnel Security Board of the
        United States Atomic Energy Commission
1958   Is awarded the Légion d'honneur by France
1963   Receives the Enrico Fermi Award from President Lyn-
        don B. Johnson
1967   Died February 18 in Princeton

SELECTED BIBLIOGRAPHY OF
OPPENHEIMER'S WRITINGS

Periodicals

"Quantum Theory and Intensity Distribution in Continuous Spectra." *Nature*, 118 (1926), 771.

"On the Quantum Theory of Vibration-Rotation Bands." *Proceedings of the Cambridge Philosophical Society*, 23 (1926), 327–335.

"On the Quantum Theory of the Problem of the Two Bodies." *Proceedings of the Cambridge Philosophical Society*, 23 (1926), 422–431.

"Quantentheorie des kontinuierlicher Absorptionspektrums" (Quantum Theory of Continuous Absorption Spectra). *Naturwissenschaften*, 14 (1926), 1282.

"On the Quantum Theory of the Polarization of Impact Radiation." *Proceedings of the National Academy of Sciences*, 13 (1927), 800–805.

"Bemerkung zur Zerstreuung der α-Teilchen" (Note on the Scattering of α-Particles). *Zeitschrift für Physik*, 43 (1927), 413–415.

"Zur Quantentheorie kontinuierlicher Spektren" (On the Quantum Theory of Continuous Spectra). *Zeitschrift für Physik* 41 (1927), 268–294.

"Zur Quantenmechanik der Richtungsentartung" (On the Quantum Mechanics of Direction Degeneration). *Zeitschrift für Physik*, 43 (1927), 27–46.

"Zur Quantentheorie der Molekeln" (On the Quantum Theory of Molecules). With M. Born. *Annalen der Physik*, 84 (1927) 457–484.

"Three Notes on the Quantum Theory of Aperiodic Effects." *Physical Review*, 31 (1928), 66–81.

"On the Quantum Theory of the Capture of Electrons." *Physical Review*, 31 (1928), 349–356.

"On the Quantum Theory of Field Currents." *Physical Review*, 31 (1928), 914.

"On the Quantum Theory of Electronic Impacts." *Physical Review*, 32 (1928), 361–376.

"On the Quantum Theory of the Ramsauer Effect." *Proceedings of the National Academy of Sciences*, 14 (1928), 261–262.

"On the Quantum Theory of the Autoelectric Field Currents." *Proceedings of the National Academy of Sciences*, 14 (1928), 363–365.

"Uber die Strahlung der Freien Elektronen im Coulombfeld" (On the Radiation from Free Electrons in the Coulomb Field). *Zeitschrift für Physik*, 55 (1929), 725–737.

"Why Does Molecular Hydrogen Reach Equilibrium So Slowly?" With Harvey Hall. *Physical Review*, 35 (1930), 132–133.

"Note on the Theory of the Interaction of Field and Matter." *Physical Review*, 35 (1930), 461–477.

"On the Theory of Electrons and Protons." *Physical Review*, 35 (1930), 562–563.

"Two Notes on the Probability of Radiative Transitions." *Physical Review*, 35 (1930), 939–947.

"Selection Rules and the Angular Momentum of Light Quanta." *Physical Review*, 37 (1931), 231.

"Note on the Statistics of Nuclei." *Physical Review*, 37 (1931) 232–233.

"Notes on the Statistics of Nuclei." With P. Ehrenfest. *Physical Review*, 37 (1931), 333–338.

"Relativistic Theory of the Photoelectric Effect. Part II—Photoelectric Absorption of Ultragamma Radiation." With Harvey Hall. *Physical Review*, 38 (1931), 57–79.

"Note on Light Quanta and the Electromagnetic Field." *Physical Review*, 38 (1931), 725–746.

"On the Range of Fast Electrons and Neutrons." With J. F. Carlson. *Physical Review*, 38 (1931), 1787–1788.

———— (Abstract). *Physical Review*, 39 (1932), 864–865.

"The Impacts of Fast Electrons and Magnetic Neutrons." With J. F. Carlson. *Physical Review*, 41 (1932), 763–792.

"The Disintegration of Lithium by Protons." *Physical Review*, 43 (1933), 380.

"On the Production of the Positive Electron." With M. S. Plesset. *Physical Review*, 44 (1933), 53–55.

"The Production of Positives by Nuclear Gamma-Rays." With Leo Nedelsky. *Physical Review*, 44 (1933), 948–949.

———— (Abstract). *Physical Review*, 45 (1934), 136.

———— (Errata). *Physical Review*, 45 (1934), 283.

"On the Theory of the Electron and Positive." With W. H. Furry. *Physical Review*, 45 (1934), 245–262.

———— (Letter). *Physical Review*, 45 (1934), 343–344.

———— (Abstract). *Physical Review*, 45, (1934), 290.

"On the Limitation of the Theory of the Positron." With W. H. Furry. *Physical Review*, 45 (1934), 903–904.

"On the Scattering of ThC" γ-Rays." With C. C. Lauritsen. *Physical Review*, 46 (1934), 80–81.

"Are the Formulae for the Absorption of High Energy Radiations Valid?" *Physical Review*, 47 (1935), 44–52.

"Note on Charge and Field Fluctuations." *Physical Review*, 47 (1935), 144–145.

"Note on the Production of Pairs by Charged Particles." *Physical Review*, 47 (1935), 146–147.

"The Disintegration of the Deuteron by Impact." *Physical Review*, 47 (1935), 845–846.

"Note on the Transmutation Function for Deuterons." With M. Phillips. *Physical Review*, 48 (1935), 500–502.

"On the Elementary Interpretation of Showers and Bursts." *Physical Review*, 50 (1936), 389.

"The Density of Nuclear Levels." With R. Serber. *Physical Review*, 50 (1936), 391.

"On Multiplicative Showers." With J. F. Carlson. *Physical Review*, 51 (1937), 220–231.

"The Disintegration of High Energy Protons." With G. Nordheim, L. W. Nordheim, and R. Serber. *Physical Review*, 51 (1937), 1037–1045.

"Note on the Nature of Cosmic Ray Particles." With R. Serber. *Physical Review*, 51 (1937), 1113.

"Note on Nuclear Photoeffect at High Energies." With F. Kalckar and R. Serber. *Physical Review*, 52 (1937), 273–278.

"Note on Resonances in Transmutations of Light Nuclei." With F. Kalckar and R. Serber. *Physical Review*, 52 (1937), 279–282.

"Note on Boron Plus Proton Reactions." With R. Serber. *Physical Review*, 53 (1938), 636–638.

"On the Stability of Stellar Neutron Cores." With R. Serber. *Physical Review*, 54 (1938), 540.

"On Massive Neutron Cores." With G. M. Volkoff. *Physical Review*, 55 (1939), 374–381.

"On Continued Gravitational Contraction." With H. Snyder. *Physical Review*, 56 (1939), 455–459.

"On Pair Emission in the Proton Bombardment of Fluorine." With J. S. Schwinger. *Physical Review*, 56 (1939), 1066–1067.

Discussion of "The Behavior of High Energy Electrons in the Cosmic Radiation," by C. G. Montgomery and D. C. Montgomery. *Review of Modern Physics*, 11 (1939), 264–266.

"Celebration of the Sixtieth Birthday of Albert Einstein." *Science*, 89 (1939), 335.

"The Production of Soft Secondaries by Mesotrons." With H. Snyder and R. Serber. *Physical Review*, 57 (1940), 75–81.

"On the Applicability of Quantum Theory to Mesotron Collisions." *Physical Review*, 57 (1940) 353.

"On the Spin of the Mesotron." *Physical Review*, 59 (1941), 462.

"On the Selection Rules in Beta-Decay." *Physical Review*, 59 (1941), 908.

"On the Interaction of Mesotrons and Nuclei." With J. Schwinger. *Physical Review*, 60 (1941), 150–152.

"Internal Conversion in Photosynthesis." *Physical Review*, 60 (1941), 158.

"The High Energy Soft Component of Cosmic Rays." With R. Christy. *Physical Review*, 60 (1941), 159.

"Multiple Production of Mesotrons by Protons." With E. Nelson. *Physical Review*, 60 (1941), 159–160.

"On the Internal Pairs from Oxygen." *Physical Review*, 60 (1941), 164.

"Pair Theory of Meson Scattering." With E. Nelson. *Physical Review*, 61 (1942), 202.

"Reaction of Radiation on Electron Scattering and Heitler's Theory of Radiation Damping." With H. A. Bethe. *Physical Review*, 70 (1946), 451–458.

"The Multiple Production of Mesons." With H. W. Lewis and S. A. Wouthuysen. *Physical Review*, 73 (1948), 127–140.

"Note on Stimulated Decay of Negative Mesons." With S. T. Epstein and R. J. Finkelstein. *Physical Review*, 73 (1948), 1140–1141.

"Discussion on the Disintegration and Nuclear Absorption of Mesons. Remarks on μ-Decay." *Review of Modern Physics*, 21 (1949), 34–35.

"Internal Conversion in the Photosynthetic Mechanism of Blue Green Algae." With William Arnold. *Journal of General Physiology*, 33 (1959), 423–435.

"Thirty Years of Mesons." *Physics Today*, 19 (1966), No. 11, 51.

Books

"The Mesotron and the Quantum Theory of Fields." In Enrico Fermi *et al.*, *Nuclear Physics*. Philadelphia: University of Pennsylvania Press, 1941.

"The New Weapon: The Turn of the Screw." In Dexter Masters

and Katharine Way (eds.), *One World or None*. New York: McGraw-Hill Book Company, 1946.

Science and the Common Understanding (The B.B.C. Reith Lectures, 1953). London: Oxford University Press; New York: Simon and Schuster, Inc., 1954.

The Open Mind. New York: Simon and Schuster, Inc., 1955.

Jews in the World of Science. New York: Monde, 1956.

The Constitution of Matter. Eugene, Ore.: Oregon State System of Higher Education, 1956.

The Flying Trapeze: Three Crises for Physicists. London: Oxford University Press, 1964.

INDEX

About the Authors

I. I. RABI was Professor of Physics at Columbia University from 1937 until his appointment as University Professor at Columbia in 1964. He has been University Professor Emeritus since 1967. Dr. Rabi received the Nobel Prize in Physics in 1944 for the resonance method of recording the magnetic properties of atomic nuclei.

ROBERT SERBER is one of the founders of the Los Alamos Laboratories and the theoretical physicist who accompanied the first atomic bomb across the Pacific. Since 1951 he has been Professor of Physics at Columbia University.

VICTOR F. WEISSKOPF was affiliated with the Manhattan Project from 1943 to 1946. An authority on nuclear structure, he is Physics Chairman and Institute Professor at Massachusetts Institute of Technology. From 1960 until 1965 he served as Director-General of CERN while on leave from Massachusetts Institute of Technology.

ABRAHAM PAIS is one of the founding fathers of particle physics. He came to the Institute for Advanced Study at Princeton from the Institute of Theoretical Physics, Copenhagen, and held a professorship there from 1950 until 1963. He is presently a professor at The Rockefeller University.

GLENN T. SEABORG was associated with the University of California, Berkeley, during the Oppenheimer years. In 1942 he headed plutonium work at the Metallurgical Laboratory of the University of Chicago. He was co-recipient of the Nobel Prize for Chemistry with Edwin M. McMillan in 1951 for their discoveries in the chemistry of the transuranium elements. He is now Chairman of the United States Atomic Energy Commission.